THE WORLD OF
ROBOTS

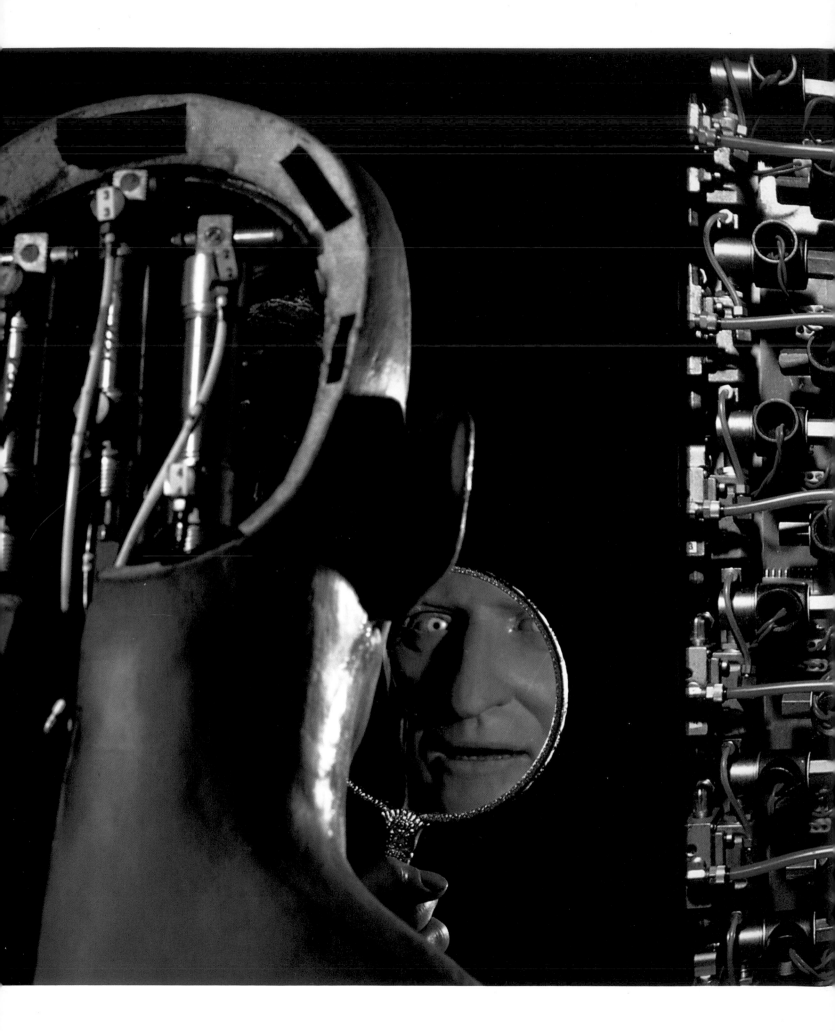

THE WORLD OF
ROBOTS

BRIAN MORRIS

ROBOTS ROBOTS ROBOTS ROBOTS ROB

GALLERY BOOKS
An Imprint of W. H. Smith Publishers Inc.
112 Madison Avenue
New York City 10016

This book was devised and produced by
Multimedia Publications (UK) Ltd

Editor: Anthony J. Lambert
Production: Karen Bromley
Design: Terry Allen
Picture Research: Mary Fane and Virginia
Landry
Technical Research: Gero Vasco

Copyright © Multimedia Publications (UK) Ltd
1985

First published in the United States of America
1985 by Gallery Books, an imprint of W.H. Smith
Publishers Inc., 112 Madison Avenue, New York,
NY 10016

ISBN 0 8317 9566 2

Typeset by Keene Graphics
Origination by Imago
Printed in Italy by Sagdos

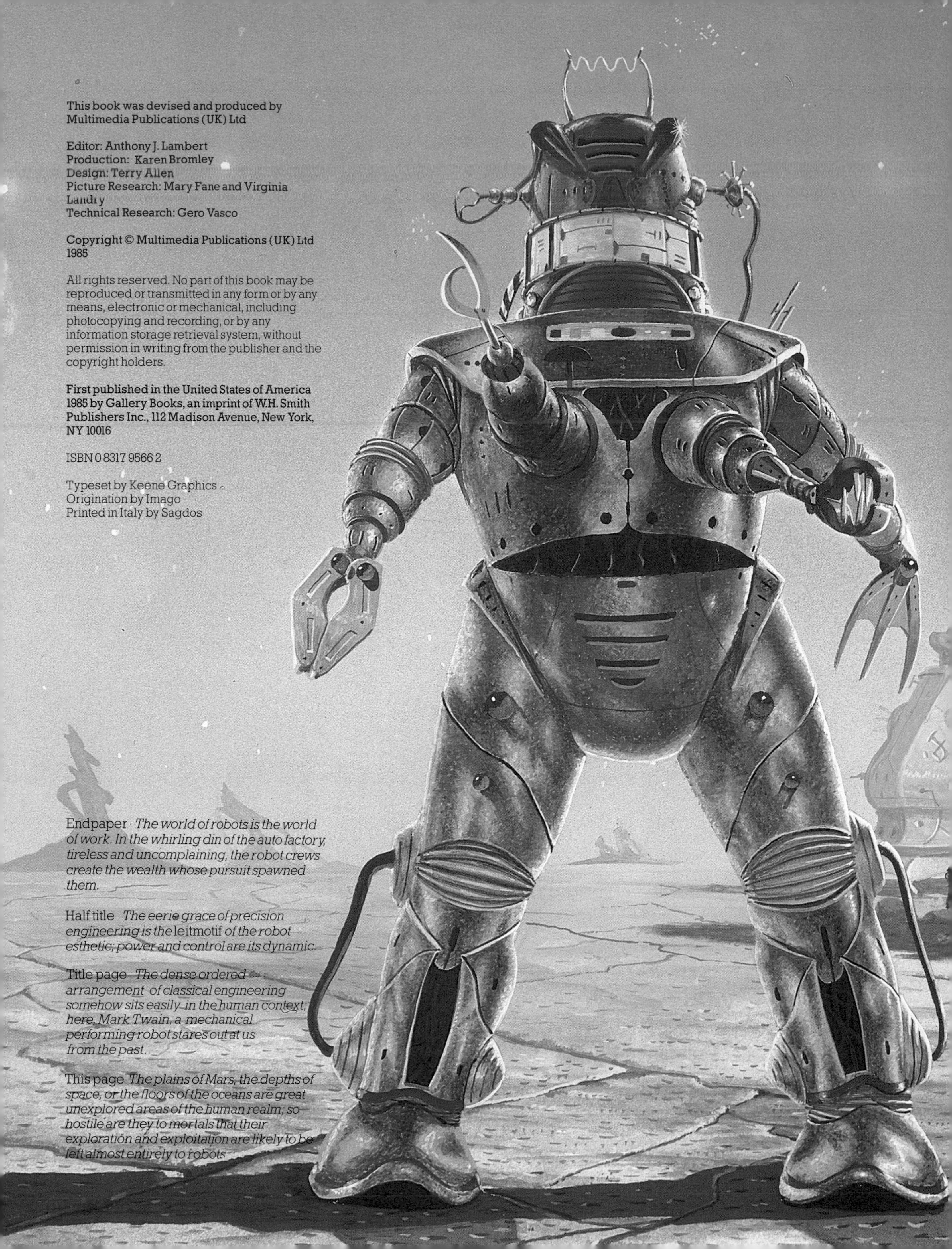

Endpaper *The world of robots is the world
of work. In the whirling din of the auto factory,
tireless and uncomplaining, the robot crews
create the wealth whose pursuit spawned
them.*

Half title *The eerie grace of precision
engineering is the leitmotif of the robot
esthetic; power and control are its dynamic.*

Title page *The dense ordered
arrangement of classical engineering
somehow sits easily in the human context;
here, Mark Twain, a mechanical
performing robot stares out at us
from the past.*

This page *The plains of Mars, the depths of
space, or the floors of the oceans are great
unexplored areas of the human realm; so
hostile are they to mortals that their
exploration and exploitation are likely to be
left almost entirely to robots*

CONTENTS

Introduction

Introduction:

The Robot Imperative

"That two-handed engine at the door…"
'Lycidas' — *J. Milton*

"Ladies and gentlemen — Meet the future!" — the portentous but telling words of the traveling salesman in *Butch Cassidy and the Sundance Kid* as he introduces the crowd to the safety bicycle. They are as appropriate now in a book on robots as they were then in a film about outlaws.

We in the western world live in an industrialized, stratified society facing the promise and the problems of a post-industrial future in which the robot seems to offer either an inexhaustible source of cheap uncomplaining labor or else one more insidious threat to industrial employment and working-class prosperity; the salesman's audience lived in the Old West just as the Frontier was closing, as pioneering gave way to production, and the factories of the East and Mid-West began to turn out cheap, mass-produced consumer goods that would irrevocably transform the isolated bucolic existence of the typical North American. The bicycle was the first mechanized personal transport, affordable by anyone in employment irrespective of status or class; it was the forerunner of the automobile, the washing machine, the television, the telephone, the computer — all the household technology which the affluent sections of the twentieth-century world take for granted but upon which our leisurely, peaceful, ways of life depend utterly.

Naturally, that bicycle salesman was no altruistic missionary, despite his spiel; he was there, hundreds of miles from paved streets and tramcars, in some cow-town in the middle of nowhere, at the behest of exactly the force that has the robot knocking at our doors today — the profit motive. Bicycles could be made more cheaply than the horses that they could more or less replace, so entrepreneurs built factories to make bicycles, and sent their salespeople across the face of the world to sell them — never mind the future or the social implications — the business of business is business! Come forward in time a century, for bicycle read robot, for horse read worker, and both the title and the cautionary rubric of this chapter are explained. The fruits of mechanization are certainly plentiful, but they are also strongly flavored, with more than a hint of sourness.

Just as the first stages of industrialization which produced the bicycle brought personal freedom and prosperity to much of the world, so that same process brought mechanized warfare, assembly lines and totalitarian societies. William Blake's "dark satanic mills" were mighty engines of progress but the miserable lives of the men, women and children who slaved there in heat, fumes, danger and din, were the coin in which the future was bought. Cheap coal, steel and rubber made the bicycle economically possible then; cheap electricity, silicon and plastic make the robot possible today.

There may seem to be nothing dark or satanic about the sterile fluorescent-lit quiet of an integrated-circuit production line, but most of its human workers are Third-World women, still subject to unhealthy working conditions, economic exploitation and repressive political regimes, often the more or less overt puppets of the multi-national companies that own or fund the industries whose raw material those integrated circuits are. The unemployed manual and semi-skilled workers all over the world whose jobs have been taken over by automated, computerized and (increasingly) robotic machines may not starve in their state-supported idleness, but neither are they likely to see themselves as the citizens of a new Periclean Athens, leisured and cultivated members of an élite society, freed from daily toil by the uncomplaining drudgery of armies of robot slaves.

Two hundred years of industrial development may have made us wary, if not actually cynical, about the possible social costs of robots, but the myths and folk-tales of history should be enough to close the subject once and for all. The image of the created being turning upon itself or its creator with dire results is thousands of years old, and common to most cultures.

Opposite The most significant machines are not always the most complicated, nor the most powerful. The mass-produced bicycle of the nineteenth century brought personal transport within the reach of most wage-earners; the "slavery" of the factory system brought forth the freedom of the roads. Humans have always been ready to make that kind of a deal, and the robot seems to be the bargain of the century; do we really know the terms, and can we afford the payments?

CYCLING IS LIKE FLYING.

THE BEST WHEEL.

COLUMBIA BICYCLES

It runs Ahead of ALL Other Cycles FOR LIGHTNESS, STRENGTH, & ELEGANCE.

Manufactured by the

POPE MANUFACTURING CO., HARTFORD U.S.A.

The archetypal rogue robot is perhaps the golem of Judaic myth. The word is used in the Talmud (the collection of rabbinical writings on scriptural, civic and moral matters dating back to the Babylonian and Egyptian captivities during the first and second millenia BC) to describe Adam as the shapeless clay into which the Creator breathed life. Rabbi Löw of Prague in 1580 is supposed to have raised such a golem and employed him as a servant in the synagogue until his developing sense of identity and rebellion forced the Rabbi to return him to the clay at the age of thirteen.

Sanskrit myth of similar antiquity tells of the creation of a female humanoid called Tilottama whose beauty is such that two of the gods are killed fighting over her. Later stories tell of a mysterious smith creating lamas and monks of gold, kings and courtiers of bronze, melodious choirs of silver, and soldiers of bronze. By the Middle Ages such robots are common figures in Indian myth as the products of human artifice — mechanical marvels of wood and metal.

Greek legend tells of Pygmalion, king of Cyprus, who falls in love with Galatea, a beautiful ivory statue. Aphrodite, goddess of beauty, brings Galatea to life so that the king may marry her — a happy outcome in this original version but one cursed with jealousy and resentment in subsequent re-tellings by W. S. Gilbert *(Pygmalion and Galatea)*, G.B. Shaw *(Pygmalion)* and Lerner and Loewe *(My Fair Lady)*.

Later Greek myths feature the first robot engineers, Hephaestus and Daedalus. The former created many mechanical humanoids, foremost among them being Talos, the giant bronze guardian of the beaches of Crete who hugged his enemies to death in his red-hot bosom, but died when his vital fluids drained away through his heel. Daedalus was the legendary Athenian inventor who built the Cretan Labyrinth, invented the saw, the axe and the gimlet, and created a wooden sculpture that he brought to life by pouring mercury into its veins. His genius had tragic reward when his son, Icarus, took flight on Daedalus's marvelous wings, and, flying too close to the sun in his unthinking trust, fell to his death. If we are to admire the Greeks in their slave-supported ease, we should at least assume some of their suspicion of technology.

The classic robot tragedy of modern western myth is, of course, Frankenstein's monster in Mary Shelley's story. The eponymous scientist creates his golem from human flesh and animates it by lightning, only to see it become a child-killing monster which ultimately turns upon Frankenstein himself. Virtually every robot story written since has followed this pattern of creation, rebellion, and disaster.

These powerful stories obviously bespeak a deeply felt human urge which engineers have long since labored to fulfil. Despite the Greek myths described above, the engineers of antiquity had neither the materials nor the methods necessary for robot engineering, though Hero of Alexander, inventor of the steam turbine, built ingenious mechanical tableaux powered by air or water featuring moving human and animal figures. The first true automaton seems to have been the mechanical duck of Jacques de Vaucanson, presented to the Academie Royale des Sciences in Paris in 1738. The duck flapped its wings, quacked, ate and shat; the Academiciens' reactions are not recorded.

Left *The long love affair between humans and their machines has had its trying moments; Charlie Chaplin's* Modern Times *is today a bitter-sweet evocation of a vanishing industrial culture now being replaced by the more complex relationships of the robotic era.*

Right *Robot images recur through mechanical history; this orthopedic apparatus of the seventeenth century is an eerie precursor of the robots of the twentieth. C3PO would certainly admire the knee joints.*

Below *Jacques de Vaucanson's mechanical duck, built in 1738, was typical of the automata toys of the period, a true member of a line stretching back to pre-Christian Greece. Engineers have always built simulations of people and animals; if not always with the precision of this quacking, flapping, splashing simulacrum, yet certainly with the same creative intent.*

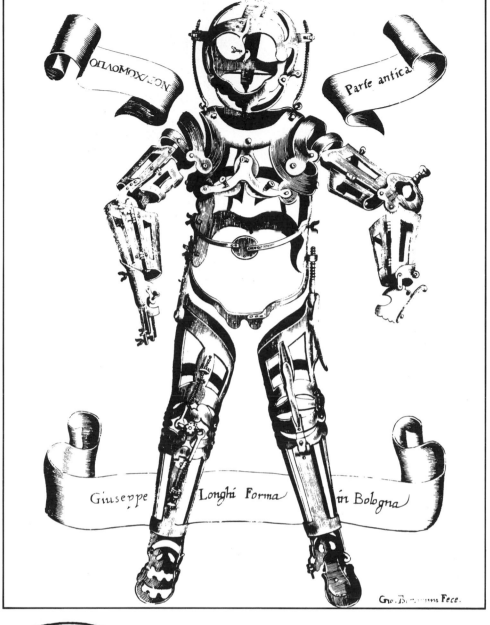

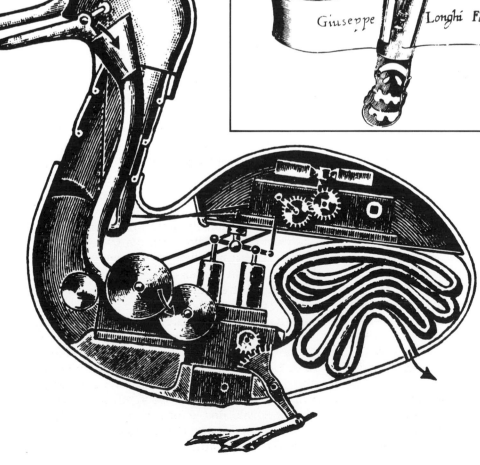

Top *Still working after two hundred years,
The Writer was built by the ingenious Jacquet-
Droz family to dip its pen, shake off the ink,
and write Descartes' rubric, "I think therefore
I am", in Latin copperplate.*

Right *Robotics is the science of control, and
feedback is its essence. The principle is
clearly seen in James Watt's steam governor:
as the engine speed rises so the whirling
balls rise with respect to the shaft; their
linkage moves a steam input valve which
controls the speed, preventing the engine
from running too fast or too slow.*

Right *The second essential of robotics is computing power. Charles Babbage invented most of the principles of computing in the early nineteenth century, but lacked the technology to put his ideas into effect. He succeeded in gaining British government support for his research, however, which many regard as his finest achievement.*

Below *In attempting to mechanize the tedious and error-prone calculations which the growing sciences of engineering, navigation and astronomy necessitated, Babbage made ambitious plans for a mechanical computer. Called the Difference Engine, made of cogs and powered by steam, it was never built, though Babbage spent twenty years trying.*

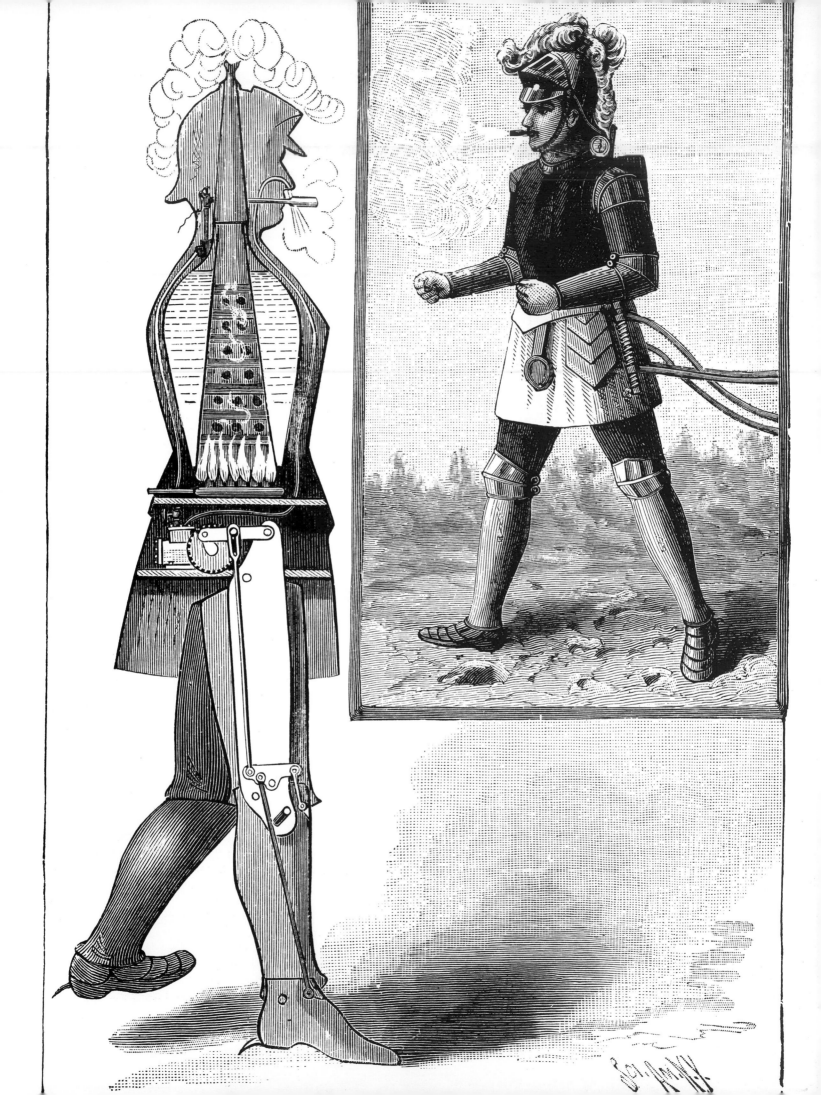

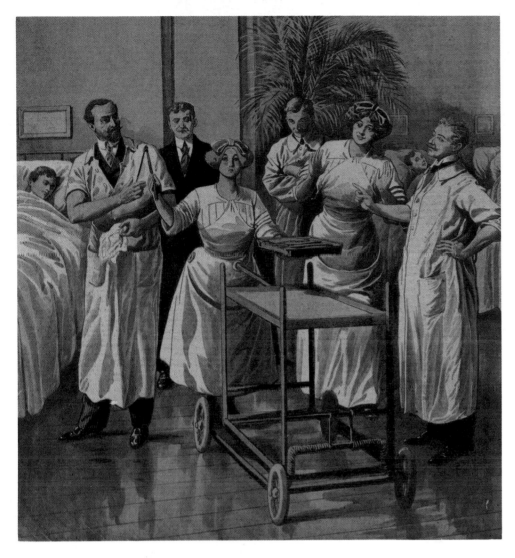

Working at the same time as de Vaucanson was the Swiss inventor Pierre Jacquet-Droz, creator of puppets and mechanical marvels. His most celebrated automaton, The Writer, survives in a Neuchâtel museum, and is a beautifully constructed model of a young man seated at a writing desk. He dips his pen into the inkwell and in a good clerk's hand writes "Cogito Ergo Sum" ("I think therefore I am"). This choice of apothegm is a fitting homage to its author, René Descartes, the seventeenth-century philosopher, since he himself is supposed to have created a mechanical servant-woman called Francine, who was thrown into the sea by a superstitious sailor.

As the engineering skills of the nineteenth century expanded the mechanical possibilities, so the range of simulacra and automata became more diverse: from The Turk, the mechanical chess-player that actually contained a small man, to the steam-driven man invented by George Moore in Britain in 1892, capable of a claimed 8mph walk over level ground, wind-assisted. None of them, however, had any practical use; real working robots had to wait on the essentially twentieth-century developments of electricity, alloy and plastic technology, and, most important of all, computers.

The story of modern robots, the semi- or pseudo-intelligent autonomous automata that the word really means to most of us, is actually the story of computers in mobile form. Without the decision-making logical power of computers, a mechanical man is just a moving curiosity; contrariwise, the computer is fine as a simple information processing device, but starts to be significantly useful when housed in some mechanical muscle.

Just as robots had a long pre-history in myth and model-making, so the development of computers, which seems to begin only in the 1940s, actually stretches back hundreds of years — to the invention of the abacus, or counting frame, in about 2000 BC at a pinch, but certainly to the seventeenth century when Blaise Pascal and Gottfried Leibniz both invented mechanical calculating machines.

In the early years of the nineteenth century, Charles Babbage began work on his Analytical Engine, a hand-cranked calculator which embodied in its mechanical designs the essential principles of computer architecture and operation as we understand them today. He was frustrated largely by being born before the technology had developed to allow him to construct his designs. His companion, Ada Countess Lovelace, was an equally gifted mathematician and the first computer programer — with nothing to program. Apart from her place in the history of computing, her name lives on in the computing language Ada, developed in the 1980s by the US Department of Defense. Another contemporary similarly cursed and blessed was George Boole who developed in 1847 the algebra that underlies the logic of all computers.

At the same time as Babbage and Lovelace were struggling with the unrealizable future, Joseph Marie Jacquard was making it possible while making a profit — doing well while doing good — from his automatic weaving loom. This was controlled by a deck of punched cards containing a program of movements and operations. The same idea was used by Hermann Hollerith in 1890 for the machine which he built to analyze the US census returns, and infinitely greater commercial success followed. For that census of 56 million people he charged the government 65 cents per 1000 returns. In 1924 his Tabulating Recording Company became International Business Machines — IBM — the most important single body in the history of computing.

It took a world war to impel the next step in computing: the administrative needs of centralized states running huge armies and production forces spurred the development of data-processing techniques and information technology; the technical needs of the gunners and bombardiers demanded computing machinery, and the vast research efforts that produced radar and the atomic bomb also created significant new industries making advanced electronic components. In 1943 a British code-breaking team led by the brilliant mathematician, Alan Turing, built Colossus, the first recognizable computer. One hundred miles from their laboratories, the Germans were bombarding London with V1s — pilotless aircraft powered by rocket engines, steering themselves to the target by following radio beams and cutting their engines after they had measured a programed flight path from launch. This was both the golem returning to its clay and a fearsome robotic dawn.

Top *Hermann Hollerith founded the Tabulating Recording Co in 1887, and invented automatic data processing. In 1924 TRC became IBM, the world's most important computer firm.*

Left *Electromechanical punched-card sorting machines like this were used by Hollerith to tabulate the 1890 US Census returns in three years; the manually sorted 1880 returns took eleven years.*

Opposite *In 1958 Joe Engelberger founded Unimation Inc., the world's first robotics firm. Its Puma and Unimate robot arms (the two shown here painted his portrait) are world leaders in this field.*

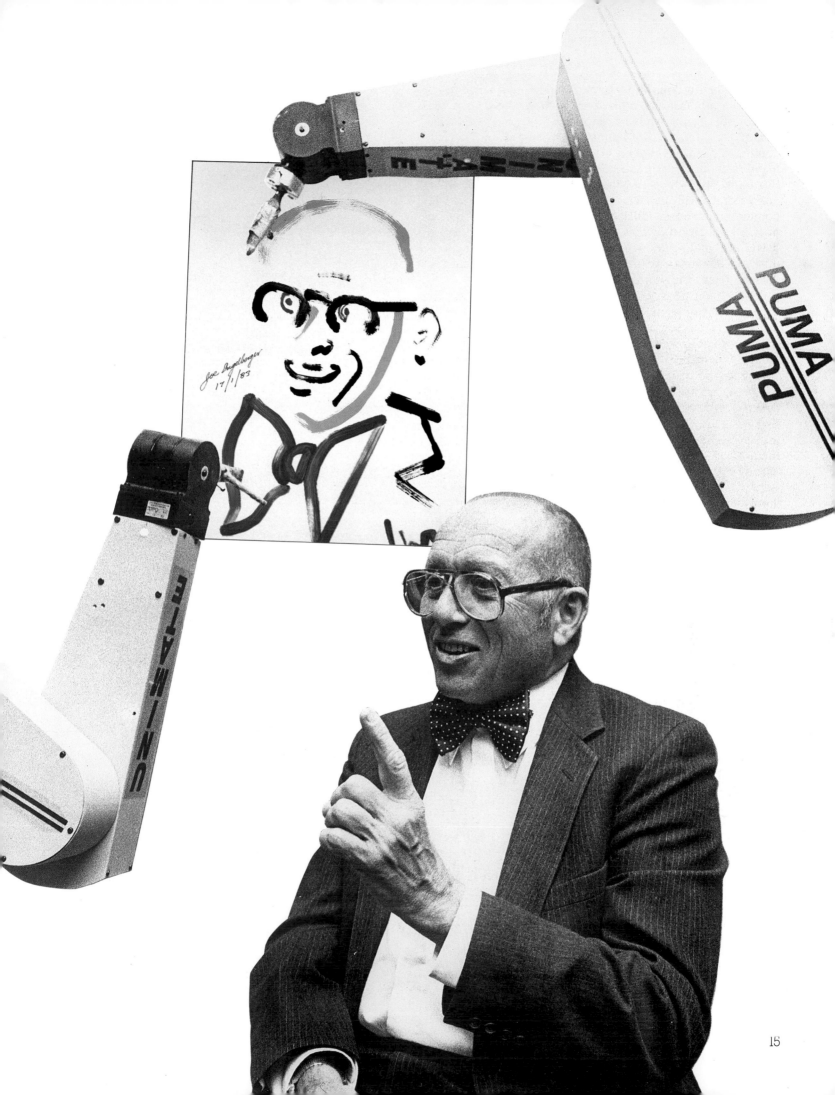

Left *Electronic computers were successfully built during and after the Second World War, but used thousands of fragile, costly thermionic valves and as much electricity as Radio City. The transistor soon put the valve out of business. Robust, cheap and frugal, they are the active ingredient of the modern computer.*

Right *This 1948 IBM Selective Sequence Electronic Calculator bears a remarkable outward appearance to the machines of today, though it is as far removed in performance as the ox-cart from the Voyager missions.*

Below *This facsimile of the first transistor, built at the Bell Labs in 1947, has all the artless charm of the lash-up prototype destined to become a mega-million seller.*

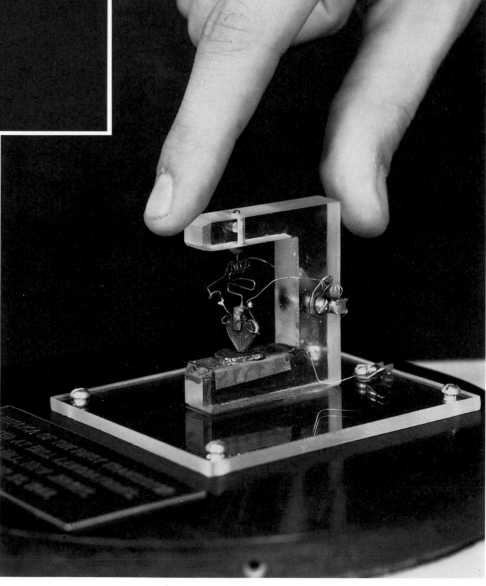

With peace in 1945 came the first true electronic computers, from teams in Pennsylvania and Manchester, England. Dependent on the bulky, fragile thermionic valves, they were made obsolete almost immediately by the invention of the silicon transistor in 1948. This marvelous machine, this motionless lump of sand and tin, whose moving parts are electrons and "holes" in space-time, is the key to the computing door. Once it came into mass-production, the whole world of computers and robots and space exploration became not just possible but certain.

The significant steps from then to this day are easily described: IBM's first computer and FORTRAN, the first popular computer programing language, were launched in 1957, and computers became affordable to business and the universities. In the 1960s the space research effort led to the miracles of miniaturization which are integrated circuits. Matchboxes could now hold computing power that the warehouse-size computers of the 1940s could not match. In the 1970s these silicon chips enabled computing's Henry Ford to produce the electronic Model T: Apple Corporation, owned by a young Californian named Steve Wozniak, produced and sold millions of cheap, robust, admirable personal computers. As the computer took over the living-rooms and studies of the West, so robots marched into the factories of the East, having become commercial reality almost by stealth: George C. Devol took out American patents on the robot hand in 1961, Joseph Engelberger's Unimation Inc. installed its first robot in 1961, and the Japanese Industrial Robot Association was founded in 1971.

Above *Apple personal computers first appeared in 1974, the first fruits of the microchip revolution. Since then home and office computers have put information processing power at every finger-tip.*

A robot killed a Japanese engineer in 1981. This tragic event, despite its human cost and wealth of fearsome symbolisms, was actually a prosaic industrial accident involving not some latter-day Talos but a commercial robot arm — nothing like the hulking steel androgyne of modern robot myth, but instead a small flexible electric crane powered by electricity and controlled by its own built-in computer. The arm, not the android, is the commonest form of today's and tomorrow's robots — 25,000 in Japan, 15,000 in the USA, 8,000 in West Germany in 1985. It is to be found paint-spraying, welding and assembling in factories across the world. The mechanical humans of popular imagination exist today but really only as curiosities and entertainments — as yet. So powerful seems to be the cultural need for the walking, talking golem-Galatea, however, that we can almost expect Milton's two-handed engine at our doors any day now. (Not that he would recognize it, since he was actually talking metaphorically about the Church of England.)

The union of computing and engineering was not sufficient to breathe life into the modern robot: that came from the new science of cybernetics, named by its virtual inventor, Norbert Wiener, from the classical Greek word for "steersman". How strongly would Rabbi Löw, Doktor Frankenstein and all those other legendary roboticists agree that the third essential of robotics is the study of control?

Wiener applied engineering insights to the study of control and communication in the human brain and body, and vice versa. Engineers and physiologists together came to see the significance of "feedback" — controlling a system by "feeding back" some of its output to itself as input. The electric current that is input to an electric heating element, for example, is controlled automatically when its output — heat — triggers a temperature-sensitive switch; the brain's output — speech — is controlled by feeding some of the sound back through the ears into the brain — the profoundly deaf person cannot control his or her voice precisely because of the missing link in the cycle of feedback. With his colleague, Arturo Rosenblueth, Wiener applied this principle to study of ataxia, a disease affecting the limbs, named from the Greek for lack of co-ordination. The two cyberneticists demonstrated that faulty feedback

Left *Captain Richards of Surrey, England built this electromechanical robot in 1928; it could stand and sit when told, tell the time, and answer (some) questions.*

Opposite *The letters "RUR" on Capt. Richard's robot allude to Karel Capek's 1917 play,* Rossum's Universal Robots *in which the word "robot" was coined. The work involved in building such a curiosity, and its success as an entertainment, both testify to the hold on the public imagination of Capek's and other robot myths.*

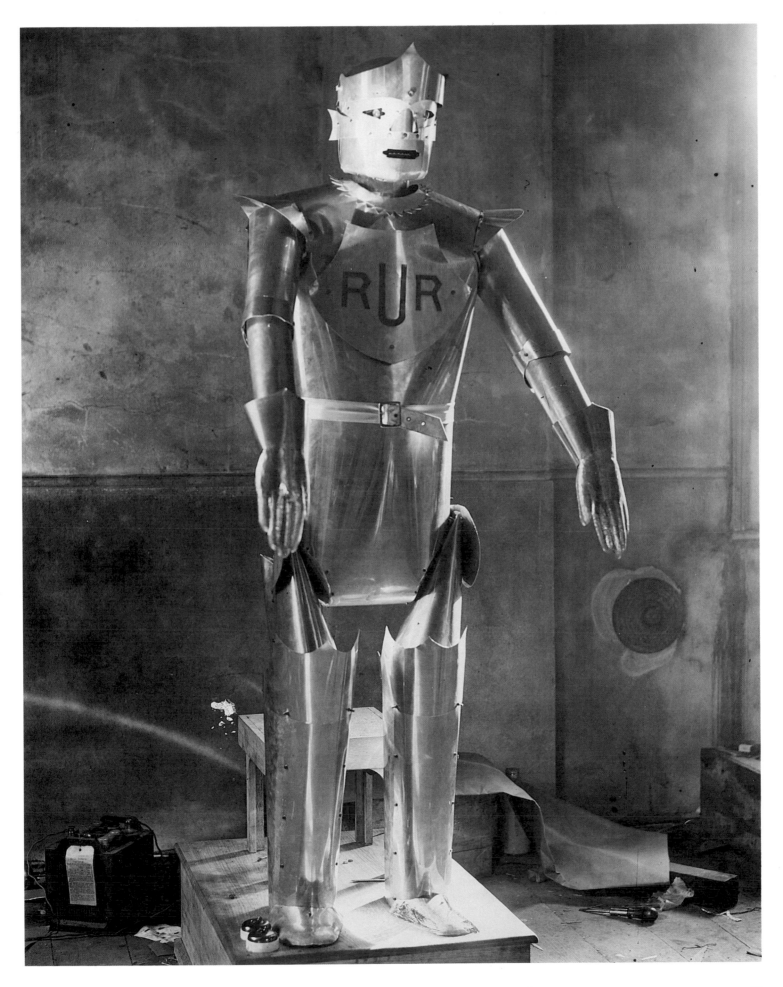

Left *Professor H. V. Wilkes, director of the Cambridge University Mathematical Laboratory, England, putting the finishing touches to the electronic brain of "Edsac" (Electronic Delay Storage Automatic Calculator) in 1947. The brain completed 100,000 different calculations a minute. Behind Dr. Wilkes are the Calculating Valves.*

Opposite *Alpha was built by Mullards, the British electronics firm, as a publicity stunt. It is seen here at the London Radio Exhibition of 1932 holding two of the company's thermionic valves, the forerunners of the transistor.*

between limb, eye and brain caused the problem, and thus opened up the human computer for inspection by engineers and information scientists striving to build robots and computers one-hundredth part as powerful or advanced. By the same token, the rigor and power of the mechanical sciences greatly increased the physiologist's appreciation and understanding of the body's functions. The British biologist W. Ross Ashby, learning from Wiener and Rosenblueth, described another vital principle of control systems when he pointed out that breathing, heartbeat and the other regular functions of the body are homeostatic (from the Greek for "staying the same"), in that their action conduces to their continued regularity: if the pulse rate increases for any reason, the increased blood pressure slows the heartbeat, just as more oxygen in the lungs displaces the carbon dioxide in the blood which triggers the breathing response — thus more breathing tends to induce less breathing, and vice versa. Wonderfully simple once someone has pointed it out.

As these scientists studied and described control systems, so they drew on the work of an American electrical engineer,

Claude Shannon, at the Bell Telephone Laboratories. He had done research in the 1930s into George Boole's system of logical algebra, and went on to develop the first articulated theory of information — that it is a quantity whose inherent uncertainty can be reduced by statistical analysis. Thus you can establish the identity of an unseen playing card from the answers to a maximum of just six "yes/no" questions such as, "Is it a red card?" and "Is its value greater than six?" Asking the Twenty Questions of parlor game and radio show fame actually identifies one million unique answers. In his work on electro-mechanical relays, the switches at the heart of telephone systems, Shannon built a model mouse, its direction controlled by relays, which could find its way through a maze by simply running straight ahead till it hit something, then turning away and trying another direction. This seemingly trivial demonstration, when combined with the power of Shannon's insights, was instrumental in forcing Ma Bell to see itself anew as selling communications rather than merely making telephones - just as Thomas J. Watson took IBM into information instead of just office equipment supply.

Left *Designed for education and entertainment, this robotic teaching machine — built by Alexander Pavlov and Galina Drozdova of Western Ukraine, USSR, in 1969 — set exams, administered tests, and supervised students in lectures.*

Opposite *This may look like a rattletrap buggy, but it's actually a "cybernetic tortoise", built in the late 1040s by British roboticist Dr. Grey Walter, and the direct progenitor of today's robots. Controlled by a simple electronic computer (notice the Mullard thermionic valve), it could sense light, avoid obstacles, and return to its hutch when its batteries ran low.*

Bottom *Yamaha's "Wasubot" brings the performing robot tradition into the 1980s. It sight-reads scores, and plays a range of keyboard instruments, including the electronic pedal organ.*

Shannon's mouse and the other information scientists' thoughts gave birth to the "cybernetic tortoises" built by the British neurologist, Dr. Grey Walter during the 1940s. These electric toy cars ran about the floor detecting light and avoiding obstacles until their batteries ran low, when they would seek out their garages and plug themselves into a power socket for recharging. That this apparently sophisticated and intelligent behavior was actually the product of trivial logic circuits and simple rules of action, was a point missed by many observers who thought them either amusing toys or the immediate precursors of intelligent robots. How fitting, then, that Apple Corporation's ground-breaking Lisa and Macintosh Computers, built in 1983, should be controlled not by typing difficult mystical words of power on the keyboard, but by rolling a toy mouse around the desk top and pointing a symbolic finger at metaphorical objects on the screen. How very apt that many of the amateur roboticists of today have cut their teeth on maze-running robot mice, built to compete in the international Micromouse competitions: in these the robot must investigate an unknown maze for a limited time, and then traverse it from entrance to center as quickly as possible.

If the young tigers of robotics are solving their real and conceptual labyrinths at this moment, the old lions (i.e., anyone who ever put on a lab coat before writing a program) realize ever more clearly the extent of the social, political and economic mazes that robots are building us. Just as the interaction of simple systems gave Grey Walter's robots the appearance of intelligence, so our own seemingly straightforward interactions with robots — we build them, they serve us — conceal centuries of myth and measureless complexities of development.

Creating Robots

"The philosophy student cries 'Damn!'
I've discovered at last that I am a creature who moves
In determinate grooves
— Not even a bus, just a tram..."
Attributed to Monsignor R.A. Knox

Our Own Image

In introducing the ideas and history of the robot image, we have failed to define a robot. The terms "robot", "automaton", "android" and "simulacrum" have been freely used as synonyms for such diverse objects as a gas-fired cigar-store Indian and a driverless crane. This evasiveness is deliberate, and reflects the imprecision and lack of agreement among roboticists in general. Popular images demand that a robot be a mechanical human capable of speech, sight, movement and independent action, but the first of these criteria disqualifies immediately the robot arm — the biggest single class of extant robotic objects; the single robotic application that produces more useful work, more real wealth, than all others combined; the one device, indeed, that roboticists, industrialists and unemployed industrial workers agree in describing as socially significant.

If we measure the robot arm against the other criteria, we find a good measure of agreement, so logic seems to advise the abandonment of the humanoid appearance, yet that seems to make the remaining definition insipid and imprecise, as well as violating common sense. Perhaps, then, any device possessed of some or all of the above qualities, and which serves a human function, or resembles some human feature, or embodies some human quality might be called a robot? Automatic chess-playing machines have most of these attributes and perform the quintessentially human function of playing chess — better than most ordinary players and as well as some International Masters. Are they robots because they move the pieces, or because they seem to think, or because they mimic human behavior? If you saw one on a toy shop counter next to a clockwork model of R2D2 that could only squawk, strut and spark, which would you say was the robot? *Newsweek* magazine spoke volumes when it said, "Now one can actually go out and buy something that looks like R2D2. But this R2D2 won't help rescue Princess Leia. In fact, it won't even take out the trash." Contrariwise, Joseph Engelberger, founder of Unimation Inc., the world's first robotics company says, "I can't define robots, but I know one when I see one." Lest that suggests that the problems of definition can be solved simply by expert opinion, he goes on to say that the official definition of the Robot Institute of America is, "If you pay your RIA dues, either your products are robots, or you are." In fact, their 1979 definition reads: "A robot is a reprogramable multi-functional manipulator designed to move material, parts, tools, or specialized devices through variable programed motions for the performance of a variety of tasks."

Unsatisfactory the RIA description may be, but it does contain the significant demands that a robot be reprogramable, multi-functional, mobile or expressing mobility, and capable of a variety of tasks. All might be argued out of court in the definition trial, but the reprogramability certainly adds a useful insight to our previous demands for autonomy.

In fact no definition will do, even the claim that one might recognize something that isn't a robot. The best we can do is to study the things that we or others say are robots, and just wait for enlightenment. Certainly the last word should go to the man who used it first: Karel Capek published his play called *R.U.R. (Rossum's Universal Robots)* in 1920, using his native Czech word "robota" (forced labor or slavery) to describe the humanoid drudges manufactured from biological material by mechanical means in the island factory of Old Rossum, a time-served, fee-paying Mad Scientist. One of his scientists says, "They've astonishing memories, you know. If you were to read a twenty-volume encyclopedia to them, they'd repeat it all to you with absolute accuracy. But they never think of anything new."

Opposite Mark Twain, a mechanical performing robot embodies the popular robot myth in his plaintive human features and resolutely mechanical insides.

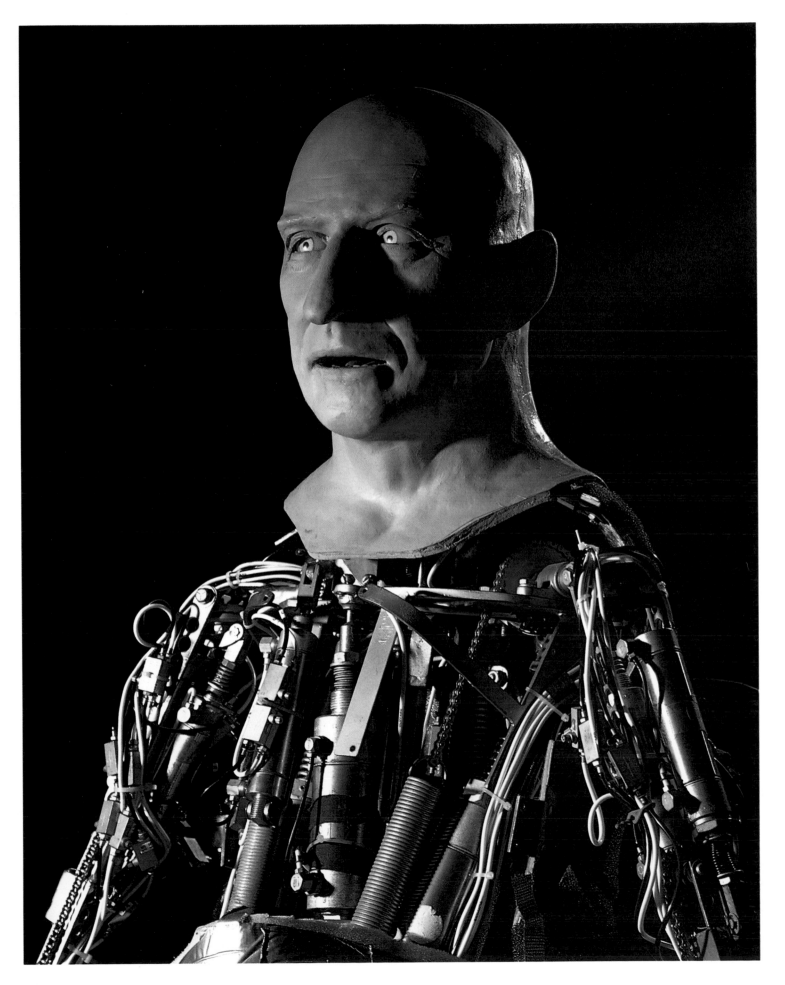

Top *The versatility of the programable robot arm is its strongest selling point; from welding autos to tending bar is just a change of software (in theory).*

Right *Specialized robots are becoming more common at work and in the home. This chess-playing computer game moves its opponent's pieces in response to keyed-in moves, and its own pieces according to its software strategies.*

Opposite *Strength is an obvious quality of this industrial robot arm, but educability is its most significant quality. The human operator is holding a "teach pendant" which allows him to move the arm through the tasks it has to learn.*

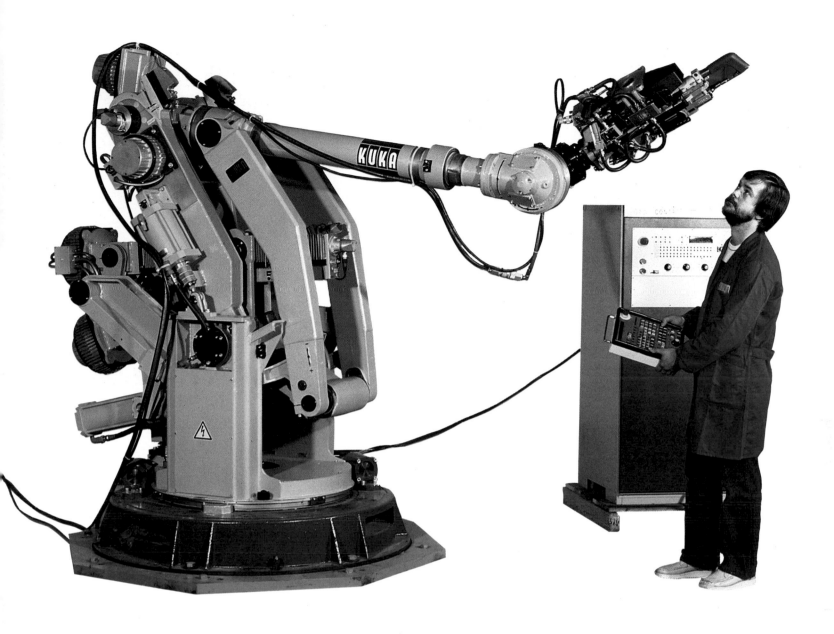

Muscle and Blood and Skin and Steel

The robot must move, or express movement, of itself or in itself. It must move, or make other things do so. Therefore it must be a mobile body or a static body with mobile members. The body of a robot, then, must contain its major organs, whether of sense or motive power. Immediately, the normal constraints of physics and thermodynamics apply to this notional robot in familiar ways:

a) If it is to move other objects, it must be powerful enough to accelerate and arrest such objects, applying sufficient force to counteract their weight and inertia.

b) It must be constructed sufficiently strongly to withstand the stresses of moving itself and coming into contact with other objects, movable and immovable.

c) Its moving parts must be sufficiently light in mass that its power plants can devote most of their output to the external task, without needing to be excessively bulky or heavy.

d) It must transmit power from its motor to its working parts through precise, controllable, efficient, adaptable drive links and bearings: all of which must be strong but as light as possible since their mass is parasitic.

Most tasks suitable for current robots demand the handling of real loads, since the economics of production processes depend upon a high-volume turnover of comparatively low-value bulk items — taking metal castings from molds, for example, might require moving a red-hot 100 lbs mass along an irregular path 5 ft in length with a vertical travel of 3 ft, three times a minute non-stop.

To get the measure of that as a mechanical task, just imagine yourself shifting a 26 ins television set in through the living-room window, under a chair, behind the sofa, and into a cupboard, keeping your feet together in the middle of the room. Imagine the kind of Goliath or Gargantua who could actually perform such a feat even once in 20 seconds, then visualize four 30-ton trucks arriving with one day's quota of TV sets. Hold a kitchen chair by one leg pointing away from you in one outstretched hand; keep your arm still and move your wrist. Try to push a car across a flat, deserted parking-lot; if you get it moving, try to stop it dead — not from in front of it though. These exercises give a very clear appreciation of the constraints that mass, leverage and inertia impose on the robot designer and engineer.

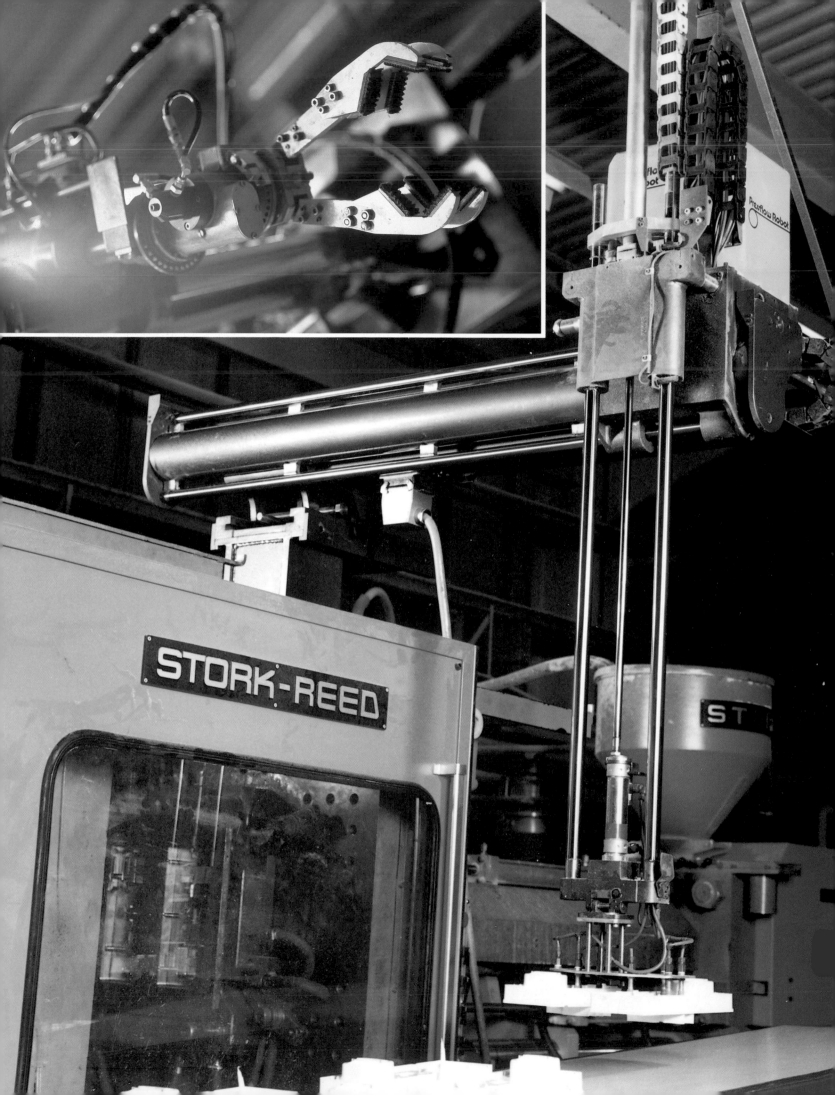

Opposite top *The pronounced claws of this hydraulically powered arm are for holding rounded objects: the gripper's wrist can rotate in two planes, and its piston-shaft forearm moves linearly.*

Opposite *Linear movement of the conveyor belt in this British injection-molding plant is echoed in the pneumatically driven "pick and place" robot arm. Compressed-air suction pads are its "fingers".*

Right *Three co-planar joints in the arm of this educational robot allow it flexibility in one plane, while the rotating gripper adds dexterity. The "Teach Console" keys show its range of programable moves.*

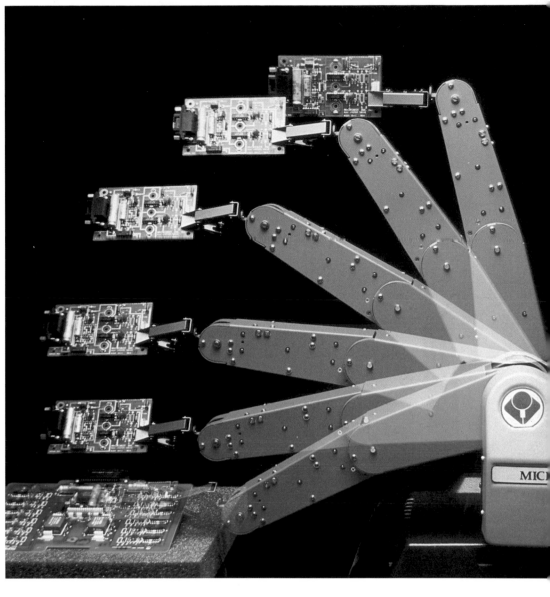

Try to compare the purchase price, lifespan and maintenance costs of a robot capable of the TV-moving task with the wages bill of the gang of normal human workers — with and without fork-lift trucks, say — who could actually shift those 1.5 million televisions per year. This gives some sense of the cost-efficiency calculations that employers must make.

Compose the speech you might make to the straw-boss of that gang when you tell him that they're all unemployed because you've bought a robot with their next year's wage checks. This helps you to understand the real social costs of automation, emphasizing the fact that doors swing both ways; it isn't always other people that pay the price of progress.

Pumping Iron

Because mass and inertia are such driving taskmasters, most robots don't have bodies — instead they have a firm fixed base which anchors them in the workplace, houses the power plants and control circuitry, and provides the fulcrum on which the limbs turn. Most robots in industrial use, in fact, are robot arms, precisely because the floor-mounted arm fits most easily into factories not designed for robot machinery, with maximum generality of function and flexibility of purpose.

The typical robot arm has at least three joints that approximate to the human shoulder, elbow and wrist: as in an anglepoise table lamp, there is a heavy base which holds the horizontally rotating "shoulder", a vertically rotating "elbow" joint, and a universal joint at the "wrist" which, unlike its human counterpart, can rotate through 360 degrees about the axis of the forearm. This is the "revolute" design, in which all joint movements are rotational. The tip of the arm moves within the hemisphere whose radius is the length of the arm when straight. It is the most versatile of the four chief designs, but it is also the most complicated — imagine that a rectangular packing case is placed within the arm's reach (its working envelope) and that the tip must follow a diagonal line inside the box, from the bottom right corner directly across the box to the top left corner. The three joints must all rotate simultaneously, but by differing amounts at every point in the path. If you watch your own shoulder and elbow joints as your hand traces such a line in space, you'll see how three angular movements are required for every linear movement. The fact that you can do it unthinkingly doesn't mean it's easy or trivial: you've had all your life to practice it, and millenia of evolution working on your engineering and programing.

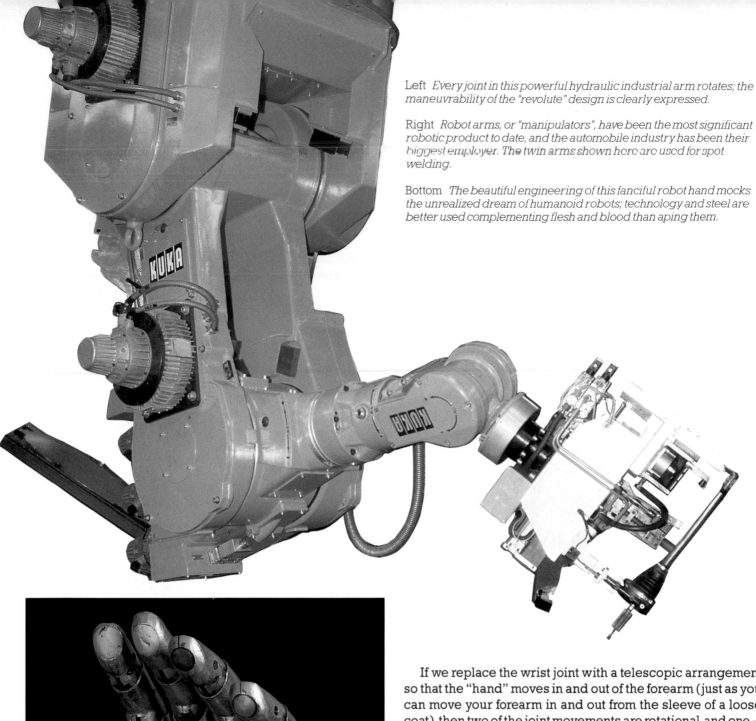

If we replace the wrist joint with a telescopic arrangement so that the "hand" moves in and out of the forearm (just as you can move your forearm in and out from the sleeve of a loose coat), then two of the joint movements are rotational, and one — the new wrist — is linear. This is the "polar" design, corresponding to the "polar" co-ordinate system of geometry, in which the position of a point in space is described by two angles and a length: these are the angles at the shoulder and the elbow, and the linear extension of the wrist-forearm telescope. The working envelope is a sphere whose center is at the center of the elbow joint, and whose radius is the maximum length of the arm, with wrist fully extended. This design would suit an arm which had to perform several simple tasks, arranged in a circle around it. Because the polar co-ordinate system describes such a space elegantly, the trigonometry used by the control system is reasonably simple to manipulate.

If, on the polar arm, we replace the elbow joint by a vertical rack and pinion system up and down the upper arm, we have the third kind of design, the "cylindrical" design. Its working envelope is a cylinder whose height is that of the upper arm, with radius equal to the length of the forearm. This design would suit a simple pick-and-place task in which the work was

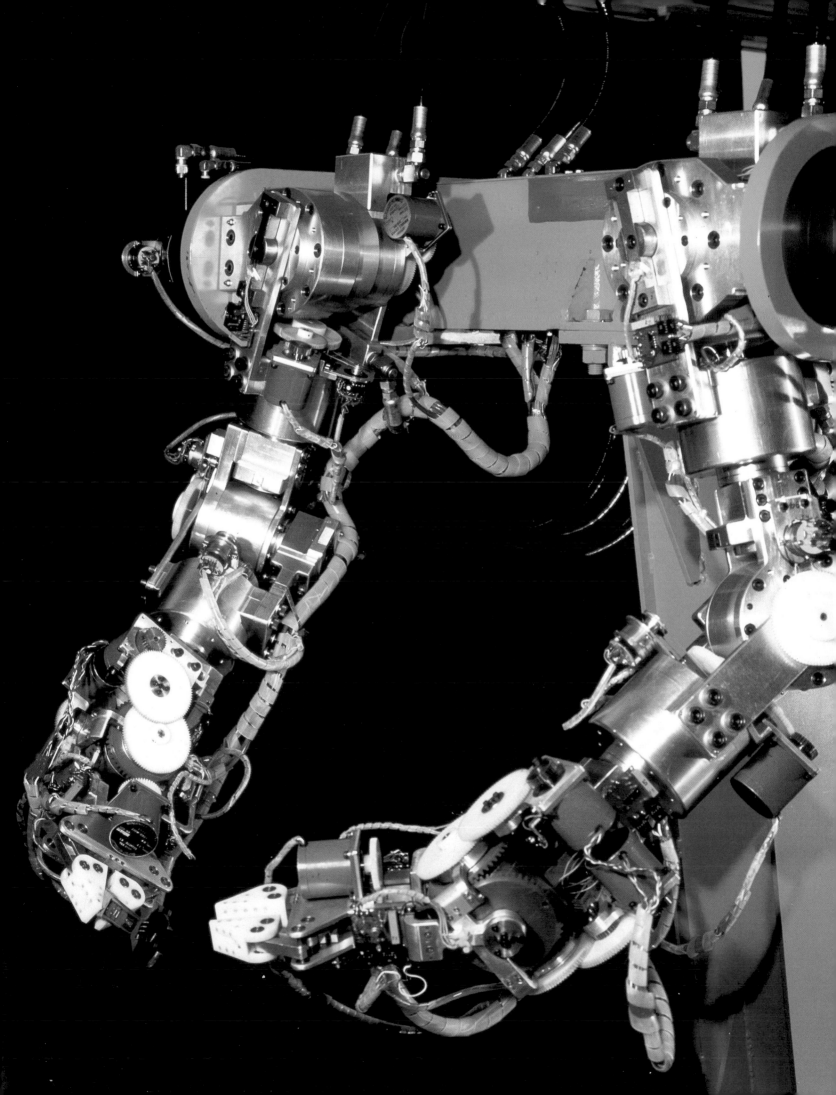

arranged in a circle around the robot; imagine a shot-firer running up and down a ladder in the middle of a circular mine shaft, pushing charges or probes into shot-holes drilled horizontally into the walls of the shaft. Because two of the joints are linear, the geometry of the working envelope offers little challenge to the programer.

Finally, in the cylindrical arm, replace the last rotational joint — at the shoulder — by a horizontal rack and pinion. Now the working envelope is cuboid, and very convenient in stacking and simple assembly tasks — picking components off shelves in a library or warehouse, for example. The design is called Cartesian, corresponding to the XYZ co-ordinate system named after René Descartes.

So much for the geometry of the archetypal arm. In practice, of course, arms take on more complicated forms because of the need to cover larger or more convoluted working envelopes than those described above. The commonest imperative is the need for greater manipulability of the "hand" on the end of the arm — notice that we have so far carefully refrained from saying anything at all about the form that it might take; indeed only the fact that we have been referring to the whole device as an arm has preserved the "hand" usage thus far. Perhaps we should introduce the common industrial practice and call it the "end effector", which sounds immediately like the very worst kind of overblown pseudo-scientific abuse of language, intended to conceal by malformation what it lacks in substance. Robotics is certainly as prone to that kind of obscurantism as any other technical field, but the usage is accurate and worthwhile for once: the range of devices that may be fitted to the tip of a robot arm is as wide and as diverse as the uses to which robots are put, and only a minority of such devices will stand the name "hand", or "gripper" or even "claw." Better by far, then, to call it the end effector and thus escape falling into the anthropomorphic trap of assuming that an arm must always terminate in a hand; so neutral and colorless a term as end effector can have no implicit meaning for most of us.

In many cases the end effector will not be used for manipulation of the workpiece: the commonest industrial robot uses are for paint-spraying, welding, finishing and assembling — most often to date in the automobile industries. In all these cases the spray gun or pneumatic spanner or grinding wheel is attached directly to the wrist, often by some kind of universal demountable system, so that other tools can replace them when the task changes. In tasks such as production assembly or machine-tool minding, the robot might need to use several different end effectors in the course of one task — a gripper to pick and place the workpiece, for example, followed by a spanner to set the tool, followed by a grinder to finish the seams. For this purpose the end effectors will be racked somewhere in the workplace, and will employ some sort of assymetric clamping method both for holding the tool and for fixing to the arm. The bayonet socket used on light bulbs is one possibility, or the sprung catch system found in socket spanner systems, for example.

Just as the range of tools that might be end effectors is huge, so there are myriad forms of gripper/manipulator end effector. The two-fingered claw, with or without touch sensors is a useful general-purpose device, but it cannot cope easily with irregularly shaped objects, especially if their shape is not

known to the programer and designer in advance. There are a number of end effectors for this and for special-purpose tasks: pneumatic suction cups, electromagnets, scoops, chain-link tentacles, airbag wrap-around devices, and so on. Some robots have two hands on the same arm, which can give huge advantages in manipulability and more than make up for the shortcomings of the general-purpose end effector.

Right *Technical and logical power are vividly embodied in the robotic union of steel, silicon, gold and thought; without the cheap computing power of the microchip the robot arm is no more than an expensive pair of sugar tongs.*

Below *Although the end effector of this Cincinnati Milacron T3 robot ("The Tomorrow Tool") is plainly designed to grip, it can hardly be called a hand, or even a claw, hence roboticists' avoidance of the term. The strength and geometrical principles of this hydraulically powered robot are forcefully expressed in the size and construction of its joints; notice the rotational wrist, the piston that drives the end effector, and the hydraulic hoses.*

Above *On quite a different scale, this British Armdroid robot arm can be made to perform real tasks, but has a load limit of only a few ounces, depending upon the task geometry. Robots of this kind are intended as educational rather than industrial tools, teaching users the principles of programing, interfacing, construction and control.*

Left *The heavy industrial origins of this Sterlitamatik robot from the USSR shape its design and functions. The operators' safety helmets are another revealing reminder of the power of such manipulators. The essential principle of robotics is control — expressed in the "teach pendant" with which an operator guides and programs the robot's movements.*

Right *An arm's degrees of freedom are determined by the flexibility of its joints, and, in conjunction with the length of the arm members, crucially affect the working envelope; this is the space inside which the arm can work. Revolute designs with 6 degrees of freedom have spherical envelopes, and can access most points in that space through more than one configuration of the arm joints; Cartesian arms with 3 degrees of freedom have a cuboid envelope and no flexibility within it; rectilinear applications, however, such as stacking, may none the less make this more suitable a design than the apparently more useful revolute arm.*

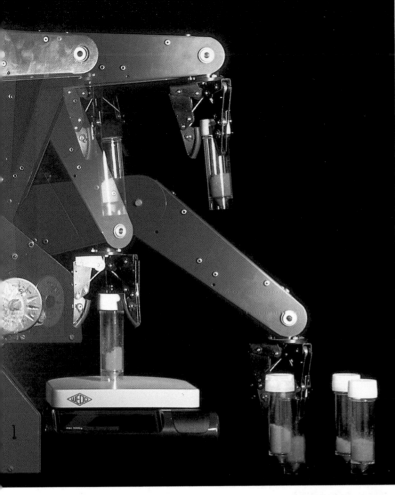

If we return to the image of the Cartesian arm traversing its rectilinear working envelope, a moment's thought reveals that the tip of the end effector can certainly access any point in that space, provided that nothing gets in the way. If, however, the arm is to do useful work in that space, then real objects will necessarily occupy it, thus barring access to some points in the envelope. Suppose that the Cartesian arm is part of an automated warehouse system, and that its task is to retrieve components from bins on shelves: if the bins are boxes without lids then the end effector of a simple three-joint Cartesian arm can only pass across the top of the bins, never inside them, or behind them. Adopting one of the other three-joint designs described above might solve the problem of getting inside the bins, but none of them is so suitable to the warehouse stacking system as the Cartesian arm. Accordingly, we add more joints at the wrist.

If we retain the three rack and pinion joints, but put a three-axis joint on the end effector, then we have a generally Cartesian system, but with a very flexible wrist, enabling a variety of conformations of the arm for access to any particular point inside the working envelope. The three-axis joint would permit the same kinds of movement as (but greater flexibility than) the human wrist. Hold your hand at waist level in front of you, palm down, parallel to the floor; you can move your hand in three mutually perpendicular planes without moving the rest of your arm. Flap your hand up and down from the wrist—this is

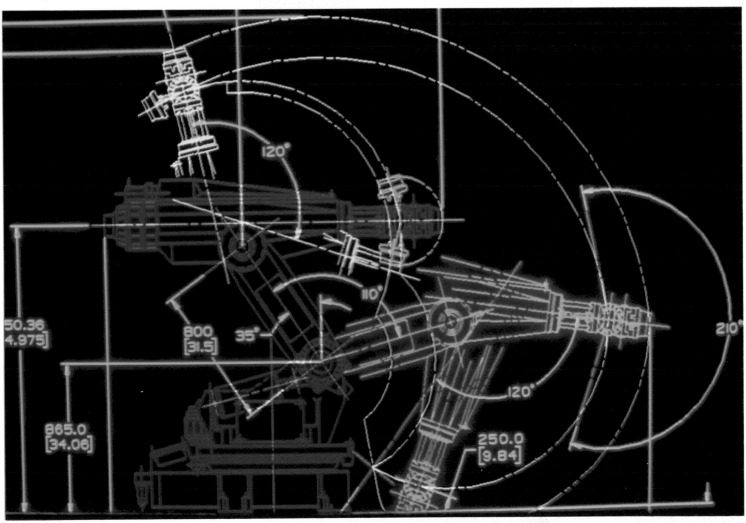

called "pitch"; wag it from left to right — this is "yaw"; rotate it from palm down to palm up — this is "roll." Notice that you do not have equal ranges of movement in the three axes. Probably you have greatest freedom in the pitch plane (about 160 degrees of swivel), and least in the yaw plane (about 70 degrees). Furthermore, if you regard the palm down, parallel to the floor position as the "natural zero" or "rest" position of the hand, you will see that movement in the three planes is not symmetric about zero. This is most noticeable for yaw: you can probably yaw 20 degrees from zero on the thumb side, but 50 degrees from zero in the little finger side. This is consistent with the general design philosophy and construction of the body, whose general symmetry is distorted locally by the needs of strength, rigidity or mobility: in the case of the hand, the opposed thumb is the most significant element — it has enabled the Naked Ape to become the Tool User, so strength and rigidity appear on the thumb side.

These fascinating details of human construction should reinforce the point made above about not calling the end effector a hand: even if it should be formed as some sort of gripper, it is most unlikely to resemble the human hand in

anything but its approximate function, so will almost certainly have symmetric movement, and great flexibility — a gripper that can turn through 360 degrees, for example, is always more useful in a robot than one with a more humanoid range. It would probably be more useful in human arms as well, but our bodies have not yet evolved that kind of technology; not because it wouldn't be evolutionarily successful, but because it's probably technically unfeasible using bone, muscle and sinew. This point cannot be made too often in robotics: the human body is a marvelously constructed machine, a miracle of function and strength, but its solutions to the problems of mobility, mass and strength are not the only ones, nor necessarily the best.

Our redesigned Cartesian arm, then, is nothing like any limb appearing in nature, yet it will fit the particular purpose very well; not merely the particular purpose, either, but a wide range of tasks in a rectilinear envelope can be undertaken by this design. It is usual to describe this arm-type as having six "degrees of freedom" or independent axes of movement: movement at the three rack-and-pinion joints is linear, while it is rotational at the three end effector joints.

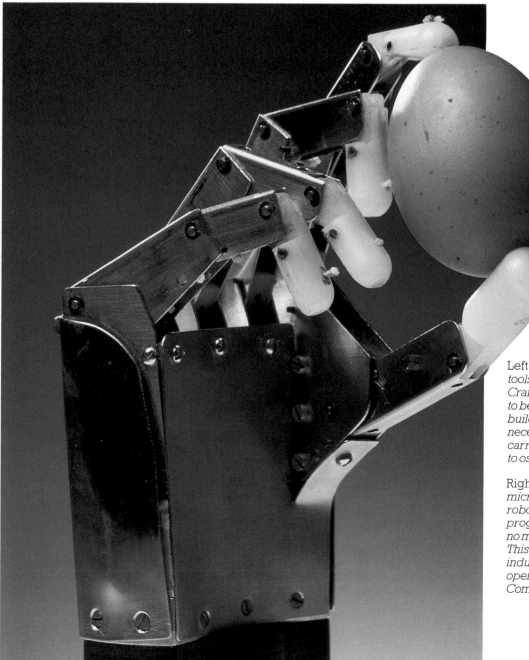

Left *Designing and engineering complex tools like this experimental hand from Cranfield Polytechnic, England, may appear to be the crucial robotic problems, but building- in the sense and intelligence necessary to a task like picking up and carrying an egg — any sized egg, from gulls' to ostrichs' — can be just as difficult.*

Right *The microchip and the microcomputer have been the engines of the robotic revolution; without their cheap programable power, robots would still be no more than player pianos or music boxes. This semi-industrial system is being used in industrial training, controlled by the operators' keypresses on the IBM Personal Computer on the desk.*

The number of degrees of freedom possessed by any arm configuration is a measure of its flexibility within its envelope, though it says nothing about the shape of the envelope. The four archetypal three-joint arms described above have very different envelopes, but the same three degrees of freedom. As we have seen in the Cartesian example, this is enough to position the end effector anywhere in the theoretical work space, but if real objects are to be manipulated there, then more freedom is essential. To investigate the effects of increasing and decreasing the degrees of freedom, try touching your right armpit and your spine between your shoulder blades with your right hand, then take a coin from your left trouser or shirt pocket, again with your right hand. Now restrict the degrees of freedom in your wrist, and try these simple tasks again. You will soon agree that five degrees of freedom may be a working minimum, but six would be a better lower limit; certainly this is conventional wisdom in robot design today.

Robot Motives

Robots need power, and, as we have seen, they need lots of it to do useful work. In the case of the robot arm, it is the geometry of the robot that exaggerates the work rate: a shopping bag or suitcase that you can comfortably carry at your side is an intolerable burden at arm's length. Furthermore, the robot arm is not a single machine with one point of application for the input power; instead, every joint has to be powered and accurately positioned. The designer, therefore, has to choose the power source and transmission medium before designing the arm.

We tend to assume that robots will be electrically powered, since it is the common motive force of our times. Certainly it is a strong contender for powering robots, but not the only one. Many robots use hydraulic or pneumatic power. There are many reasons for this choice, foremost among them being the fact that the power plant (the compressor) can be installed in the immobile base of the arm where it adds greatly to the robot's stability but contributes nothing to the parasitic weight of the arm — members, joints, grippers and joint drivers.

If the robot is to be electrically powered, the electric motors to drive the joints may be part of the joints themselves, thus increasing the arm's parasitic load, or they must be situated in the base and coupled to the joints by some kind of mechanical linkage, such as chains or cables running over pulleys, or push-pull rods, cams and levers. Another piece of jargon becomes necessary at this point: the things that drive the joints are called "actuators." Like the end effector, the term describes the device's function with no implicit suggestion of form. Thus the arm's actuators might be electric motors, or hydraulic or pneumatic drivers.

Because of the above considerations, robot designers opt for non-electrical actuators whenever the workload rises beyond a few pounds. Electrical actuators are largely confined to small-scale robots, whether for educational and recreational, or specialized precision tasks. The design dilemmas do not end with this division of utility, however.

There are many different kinds of electric motor, and the ones most useful to the robot designer are the kinds least familiar to the lay person. The electric motor that we are most familiar with — in the washing machine, say — is usually an AC (alternating current) device driven directly from the household electricity supply. This is a fine powerful motor — electricity supplies are transmitted as AC precisely because of that mode's power-supply advantages over DC (direct current) — but it has the drawback of being difficult to accelerate and decelerate with precision so is not suitable.

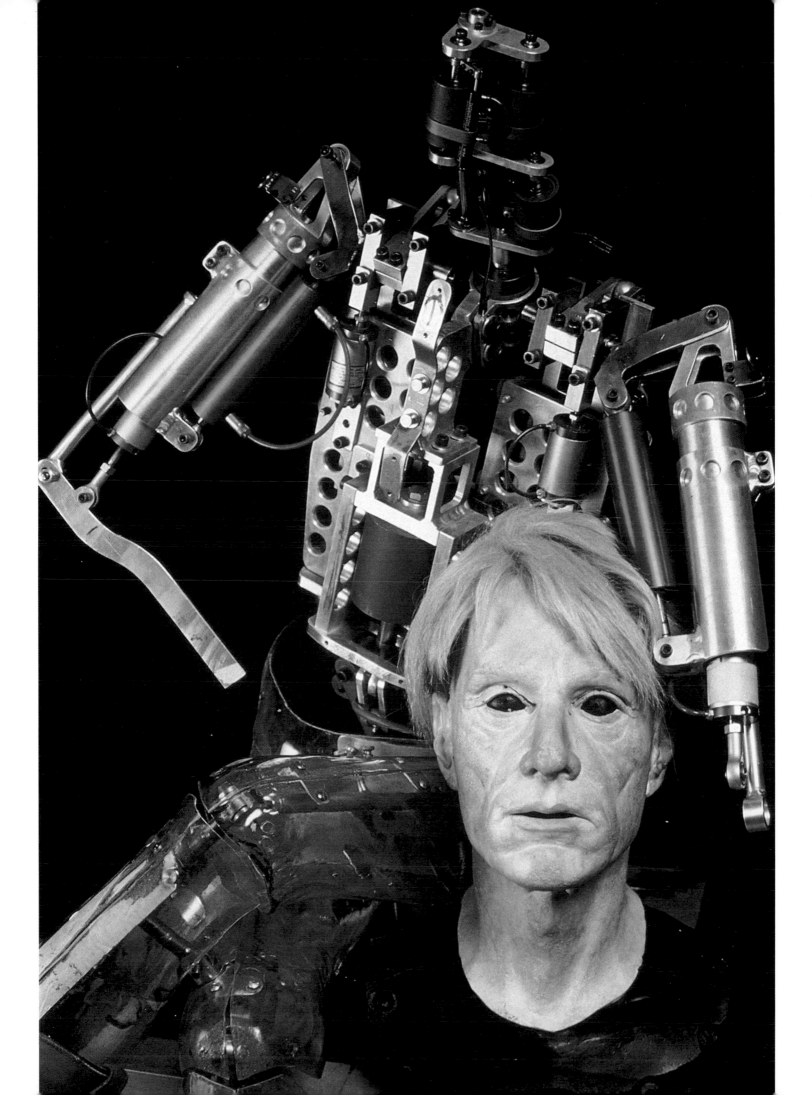

The DC motor, therefore, is more appropriate, but not usually in the form to which we are most accustomed; the kind of high-revving low-torque (low driving-force) unit that drives toy cars or electric shavers, for example. Robot arms do not need to travel at high speeds, nor very far, but they do need high torque to be able to move their own weight and that of the task load. A common choice of DC motor for robots, therefore, is the stepper motor. The shaft of this DC motor moves one precisely measured step at a time under the direction of its microchip controller. The size of the step depends upon the precision (and therefore the cost) of the unit: low-cost motors will make 12 steps per revolution (a step size of 30 degrees) whereas more expensive models may make 240 steps per revolution (1.5 degrees per step). With a motor like this as actuator, an arm can be easily driven from measured position to measured position, whether the joints in use are rotational or rack and pinion. The stepper motor is not confined to use with positional devices such as arm-joints, moreover; it can be used to drive wheels or gearboxes for floor mobiles, for example. Its controllability can be put to good use here, since the number of steps turned can easily be monitored in order to calculate distance traveled; alternatively, the system might be geared so that one step of the motor produced a linear movement of, say, exactly 1 in.

The disadvantages of the DC stepper motor spring from its torque characteristics. When the motor shaft is positioned by the control chip, the power supplied to the motor provides a torque at the shaft, and so keeps the shaft in position — obviously vital if it's driving an arm, say. If the power is turned off, however, there is almost no holding force on the shaft, so it will turn out of position under the load on the shaft, whether that be the weight of the arm itself, or that of the task. Even when power is still on, if the external load torque is greater than that supplied by the motor, the shaft may turn out of position by one or more steps "unknown" to the motor controller; the shaft may thus be 20 degrees from its zero position when the controller "thinks" that its position is 35 degrees from zero. When the load is eased, the motor will simply position itself in the nearest step position, and hold there until fresh position data comes from the controller.

For these reasons, the stepper motor may be discarded in favor of the servomotor. This consists of a DC motor, a gearshift, a controller and a position sensor. As in the stepper motor, the shaft can be accurately positioned, but only over a limited range, usually 100-140 degrees. When the shaft is sent to a given position, it moves with great torque and is held there by the controller, which constantly monitors the shaft angle as it exists compared with the angle required. If the external torque displaces the shaft, therefore, the controller will continue to apply torque in a corrective direction, and will return the shaft to its correct position when the load eases.

Left *Balance is the essence of this Japanese robot's success in climbing stairs, usually the (literal) stumbling block in any mobile's path. The pivoted antennae serve the same function as the tightrope-walker's pole, or the gymnast's outstretched arms.*

Right *This gimcrack construction is actually quite a sophisticated robot — one of the entrants to the UK Robot Table Tennis competition. The arm members are plastic waste-pipe for strength and lightness, while the motive power is provided by springs and DC servomotors — the electrical motor type used increasingly by hobbyists and development workers.*

Above Sudden movements of the table-tennis-playing robot's arm is achieved through the use of servos; the task of finding and tracking the ball in flight is handled by this vision system, in which three spinning cylindrical lenses bring the image of the ball into a binocular two-dimensional scanning grid, allowing the robot to guess at the ball's trajectory, and thus move the arm into approximately the right area early in the response cycle.

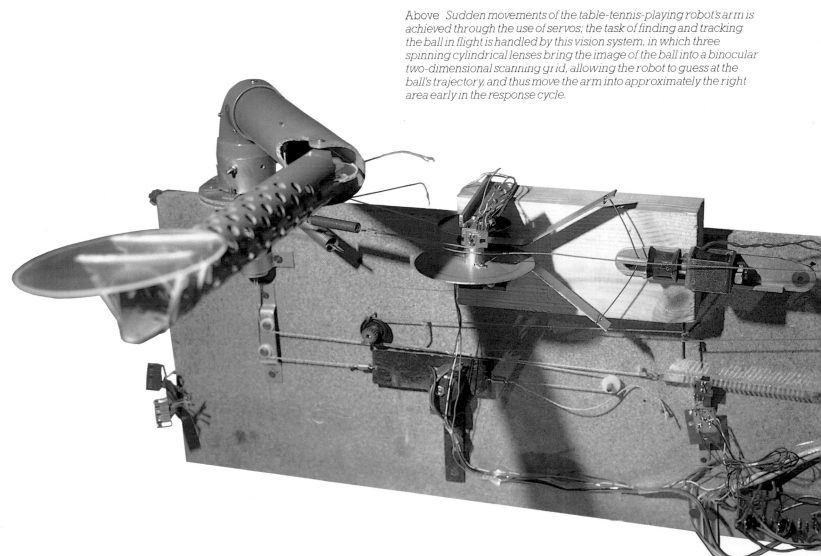

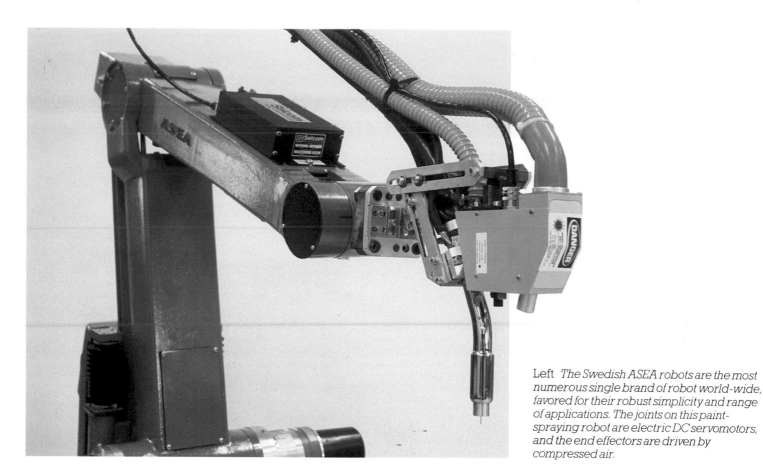

Left The Swedish ASEA robots are the most numerous single brand of robot world-wide, favored for their robust simplicity and range of applications. The joints on this paint-spraying robot are electric DC servomotors, and the end effectors are driven by compressed air.

The size of an electric motor of any kind — and therefore its weight — is generally proportional to the torque it can deliver, which is why, as we have seen, high-load arms cannot afford to carry heavy electrical motors around on their joints. Instead, they use either hydraulic or pneumatic compressors situated away from the robot, and transmit motive power to the actuators through hoses, in the form of compressed air or pressurized fluid. The general design of the actuators is the same for both media: a piston for linear actuation, and some form of turbine-like device for rotary actuation. Control is achieved through a servo valve on the input line. The advantages of hydraulic power transmission are that the power source is remote and the linkage (the hoses) is extremely flexible; that the conversion of power in the compressor to work in the actuator is efficient, especially compared with the conversion of electrical power into mechanical movement; and, finally, that comparatively low force applied to a large area in the compressor becomes an extremely high pressure on a small area in the actuator — built-in gearing, in other words. A glance at any construction site shows that robot designers are not alone in appreciating the advantages of hydraulics — every heavy tool on the site, from excavator to dump truck — uses hydraulics.

The disadvantages of this system are the size, vibration and noise of the compressor, and the slight but inevitable leakage of fluid from the actuators. An oily, noisy, crowded workplace is less disadvantageous to robots than to humans, but even fully automated factories need some human presence — as yet.

A pneumatic system is similar to a hydraulic one, except that compressed air rather than pressurized fluid is the transmission medium. Since the medium is lighter and usually under lower pressure, pneumatic systems can be less heavily built than hydraulics, and need be less finely engineered around the valves and actuators since pressures are lower.

The disadvantages of pneumatics vis-à-vis hydraulics are that they cannot deliver the same forces, and, since air is highly compressible, the actuators tend to deflect under load, making precise control of position very difficult to achieve. This last can be an advantage where an elasticity is required — in gripper claws, for example — but in general is enough to relegate pneumatic systems to a secondary role in robotics.

"But still it moves" Galileo

Useful though the robot arm is, it is not the last word in robotic devices: robots need to move as well as to manipulate. If an arm can be made mobile, then its utility may be increased ten-fold.

In fact, for all the reasons of parasitic weight and positioning discussed above, the mobile robot is difficult to construct satisfactorily, and hard to employ economically. Specialized examples do exist, of course — the Space Shuttle's RMS (Remote Manipulator System) and the various Moon, Mars and Venus Buggies being the most obviously spectacular. These are all just slave devices, however, remotely controlled by human operators. Robot vehicles must have some measure of autonomy to deserve the name, never mind to satisfy the persistent image of the robot collecting the garbage, doing the shopping, delivering the mail, patrolling the streets, etc.

The mobile robot is at present most usefully employed in specialized surroundings, where routes are either known in advance, or predictable, or defined. Automated warehouses exist, for example, in which robot vehicles climb pillars and crawl along shelves to store and retrieve stock; they move on

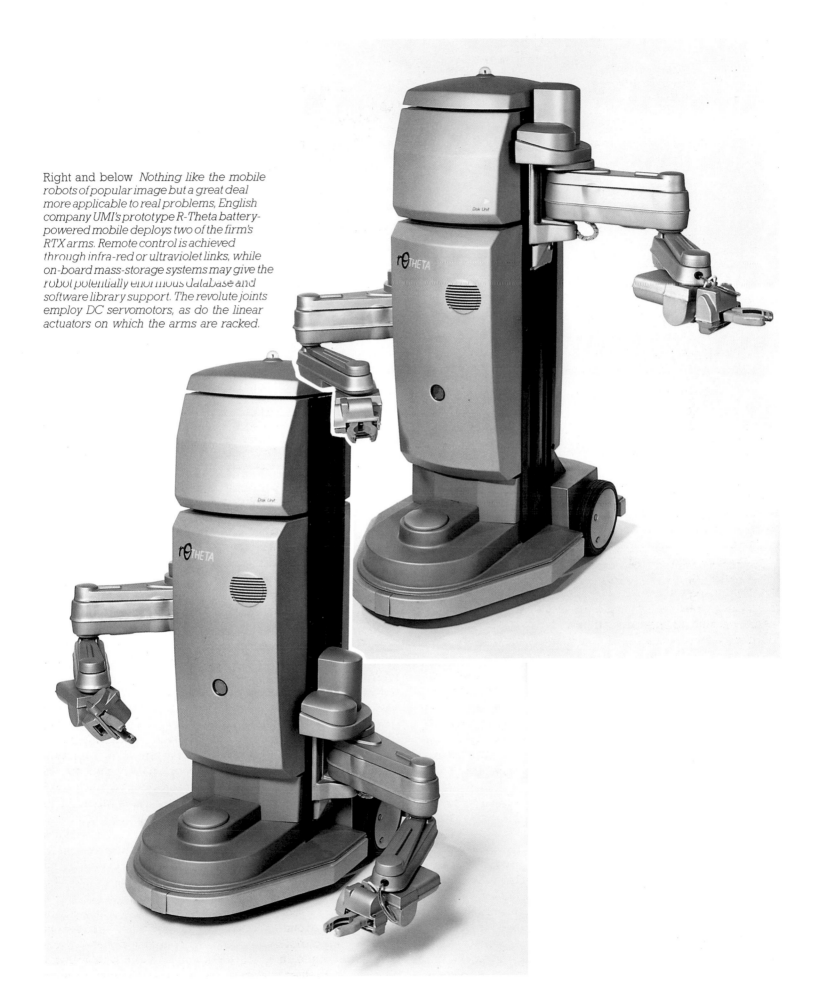

Right and below *Nothing like the mobile robots of popular image but a great deal more applicable to real problems, English company UMI's prototype R-Theta battery-powered mobile deploys two of the firm's RTX arms. Remote control is achieved through infra-red or ultraviolet links, while on-board mass-storage systems may give the robot potentially enormous database and software library support. The revolute joints employ DC servomotors, as do the linear actuators on which the arms are racked.*

43

fixed rack and pinion tracks, however, so their autonomy is constrained. Similarly, the Japanese Intellibots crawl around the shelves of the Kanazawa Industrial University library retrieving videotapes and bringing them to viewing booths. In the various Fiat car production plants, robot flatbed trucks move chassis around the factory floor; these are an example of the general class of AGVs (Autonomous Guided Vehicles), semi-smart robot vehicles following defined paths — lines painted on, or signal cables buried in, the floor.

Designing a truly mobile general purpose robot is made enormously difficult by the imponderables of the environment: what surfaces must be traversed, how will position be monitored, how will the environment be sensed? And so on. The first choice — itself really dependent on the answers to the other questions — is the manner of locomotion.

Naturally, everyone would like to see a walking biped robot, but the drawbacks are many. Programing the limbs is not particularly difficult, given that a smooth surface is always present. Introducing the kind of reflex-driven balance feedback that humans and animals take for granted enormously increases the cost, complexity and size of the robot. And to what purpose? Why, apart from sentiment, bother with legs at all? Why not wheels, or tracks?

One reason for persisting with legs is that they do permit undulating and irregular surfaces to be traversed, especially curbs and stairs that occur so frequently in human environments. The problem is that of balance. The obvious solution is to use more than two legs, but, oddly enough, research in the Soviet Union indicates that this immediately leads to reinvention of the insect — six legs are much easier to co-ordinate than four. The economics of using six legs rather than four wheels or two tracks need to be carefully judged,

though the military are known to be actively pursuing this method as the successor to the tracked cross-country vehicle.

The trouble with tracks for a cross-country robot is that in turning corners in particular, and rough ground movement in general, they are very prone to slip. Since the easiest way for a tracked robot to monitor its position would be by counting the rotations of the tracks, a tendency to slippage means built-in positional inaccuracy. This can be overcome by mounting other position-sensing devices — cheap satellite navigation systems are available now to hobbyist sailors, and auto manufacturers are talking loudly about in-car navigation systems. The problem of terrain and stability remain, though. We expect tracked vehicles to cope with all rough ground because we automatically think of battle tanks and armored personnel carriers crashing across trenches and through rivers at speed: they are large, powerful machines, however, and the military doesn't often release film of them stalled in a bog, or upside-down at the bottom of the slope they tried to cross. A tracked vehicle is limited in the irregularities it can cope with to a vertical step-size of about half its track-height, and, like all objects, will topple if the perpendicular through its center-of-mass falls outside the circumference of its base. The advantage of legs is precisely that they can cope with both of these limitations.

Wheels, of course, are possible, and are widely used on mobiles, but immediately restrict the robot to smooth, unobstructed, flat surfaces. This is no particular drawback in factories and offices, and it does not rule out the robot garbage truck or mail van, either — except that the collectors and the mail deliverer have still to move from curbside to house or apartment, and that usually involves steps, probably the largest single obstacle to the household robot development.

Left and this page *Difficult though the problems of robot legs are, many researchers have thought them worth the effort because of their potential ability to cope with rough terrain and abrupt changes of level. The Odex 1 experimental robot deploys its six legs with surprising elegance in surmounting obstacles. The legs themselves are unusual in that, by an ingenious but simple system of levers and pivots, the legs are powered by single actuators mounted on the body — the usual parasitic weight of motors or fluid actuators on the joints is saved, allowing the designers to use lighter materials in the limbs. This robot shows the way — or a possible way, at any rate, in mobiles. We take for granted the wide range of end effectors and actuators for robot arms; we should not be surprised to see as wide a range of locomotive systems becoming available, no matter how unlikely or bizarre they may at first appear.*

The Robot Brain

"…a dwarfish whole.
Its body brevity, and wit its soul"
Epigram — *Samuel Taylor Coleridge*

We have considered in Chapter 1, the problems of choosing our clay and building our golem: we must now animate it, put a brain to the arm. Naturally, this means the electronic computer, without which there would be no robotics, and no robots. So just what is a computer, and how does it control a robot?

Like the robot, the computer has no single recognizable form, and for exactly the same reason — because it is a general purpose device capable of being packaged in thousands of different ways. Like the robot, furthermore, it is associated in the popular imagination with its sci-fi and comic-book image of a room-sized collection of gray metal closets covered in switches and flashing lights, churning out piles of incomprehensible print-out and miles of sinisterly unreadable magnetic tape. Its acolytes wear white lab-coats, talk reverently about "The Console" and "The CPU", and are generally on the far side of eccentric. Mind you, that image was almost wholly accurate within living memory, but today your wristwatch contains, or is, a computer, as does your washing machine and probably your car; millions of people now own personal computers which they use for business and pleasure.

The computer system consists of a CPU (central processing unit — usually a microchip, though it may still be a filing cabinet full of discrete circuitry in large "mainframe" systems), some memory (more microchips), some controlling software (again, on microchips), an input device (usually a keyboard) and an output device (usually a TV screen, or VDU — visual display unit). The microchip seems to figure so prominently, and certainly constitutes the most important component, so we should investigate it first.

Chips or ICs (integrated circuits) are notable for the degree of micro-miniaturization that they embody, not because they do anything that can't be done with more conventional circuit components such as transistors, resistors and capacitors. They are important because they occupy so little space, take so little power and are so cheaply available, and have, therefore, brought computing power within the budget of every inventor

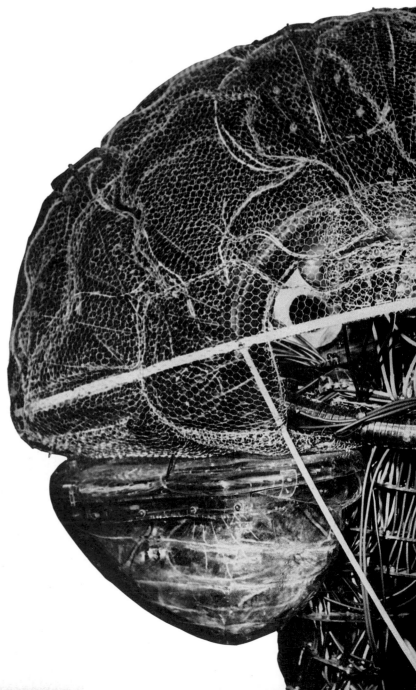

Right The complex connections of the human brain are hinted at in this greatly simplified electrical simulation designed by the Director of Vienna Technological Museum.

Above *The computer's memory consists of thousands of interconnecting transistor switches; their states represent the numbers stored in memory. The transistors are arranged in arrays inside the postage stamp sized integrated circuit chips. This one is a 64K RAM memory chip: it can store more than 64,000 numbers or characters, each of which can be changed without disturbing the others.*

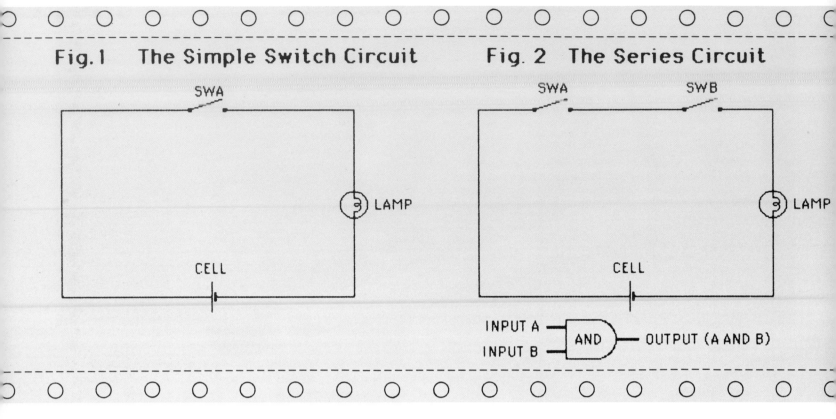

Fig. 1   The Simple Switch Circuit

SWA

LAMP

CELL

Fig. 2   The Series Circuit

SWA   SWB

LAMP

CELL

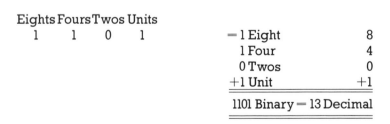

INPUT A ⎯⎯⎯ AND ⎯⎯⎯ OUTPUT (A AND B)
INPUT B ⎯⎯⎯

and manufacturer — hence their proliferation in devices which function perfectly satisfactorily without them, such as watches.

The essential component, then, whether it be a dot of silicon in an IC or a three-legged component the size of a pea on a circuit board, is the transistor, and that is just an electronic switch. Two of the wires going into it are the line to be switched (just like the two wires going into the light switch) and the third wire carries the control signal which determines whether the other two lines are actually connected together inside the transistor or kept apart; this control wire is like a combination of the light switch itself and your finger.

The transistor switch can be either open or closed, on or off, so it is called a binary device (meaning that it has two possible states, from the Greek for "two"). Since the voltage on the control wire is what switches the transistor, we can tell whether the switch is open or closed by monitoring that voltage, and conversely by controlling that voltage we can make or break the switch. We say that the control line voltage is either "high" (usually about 5V) or "low" (0V), since all that matters is whether the voltage is present or not, and we can replace the words "high" and "low" by the digits 0 and 1. Now imagine a line of four such switches which are (reading from the left) on, on, off, and on respectively. Replacing those words by digits, we find that four lumps of canned silicon are in fact representing a number, namely 1101. Now the slightly confusing part is that this is not the number one thousand one hundred and one, because it is not written in the decimal number system that we all use all the time and take for granted as the only sensible system: it is written in the binary number system in which there are only the two digits, 0 and 1, and so must be interpreted rather differently. Let's look at the decimal number first, because it will help to understand the binary system.

When you first learned arithmetic, you probably used to write your problems on graph paper, one digit per square, with labels for each column in the problem, like this:

Thousands Hundreds Tens Units

1	1	0	1	= 1 Thousand
				1 Hundred
				0 Tens
				+1 Unit

1101 Eleven Hundred And One

We take it for granted that the leftmost 1 digit here is worth a thousand times the same digit when placed in the rightmost column — the first is in the thousands column so it is worth a thousand, and the other is in the units column, so it's worth only one.

Exactly the same principle is used in binary arithmetic, but the columns have different values like this:

Eights Fours Twos Units

1	1	0	1	= 1 Eight	8
				1 Four	4
				0 Twos	0
				+1 Unit	+1

1101 Binary = 13 Decimal

Thus, the four transistors that are on, on, off, and on represent the binary number 1101, which stands for the decimal number 13. So we can use electronic devices to represent, and therefore to store numbers. This is such a significant matter that it's worth fixing it in your mind by some practice:

Transistors					Binary Number					Decimal Value
T1	T2	T3	T4	T5	16	8	4	2	1	
ON	OFF	OFF	ON	ON	1	0	0	1	1	19
OFF	ON	ON	ON	OFF	0	1	1	1	0	14
OFF	ON	OFF	ON	OFF	0	1	0	1	0	10
ON	ON	OFF	OFF	ON	1	1	0	0	1	25
ON	OFF	OFF	OFF	OFF	1	0	0	0	0	16
ON	ON	ON	ON	ON	1	1	1	1	1	??
ON	OFF	ON	ON	ON	1	0	1	1	1	??
OFF	ON	OFF	OFF	ON	0	1	0	0	1	?
OFF	OFF	ON	OFF	ON	0	0	1	0	1	?

Now if we can store numbers and manipulate them, then we have a computer. So let's return to the transistor switches, and instead of seeing them as binary digits, let's see them as switches again: we connect two switches, a battery and a bulb together like Figs. 1-3.

What difference is there in the effect of the switch positions on the state of the bulb? In Fig. 2 (called a series switch set-up) the bulb will be on if and only if [Sw.A] AND [Sw.B] are on; in Fig. 3, however (parallel set-up), the bulb will be on if [Sw.A] *or* [Sw.B] is on. If we arrange two transistors in those series and parallel set-ups, we have two devices called AND and OR Gates, and we can represent them as logical symbols, as shown at bottom of Figs. 2 and 3.

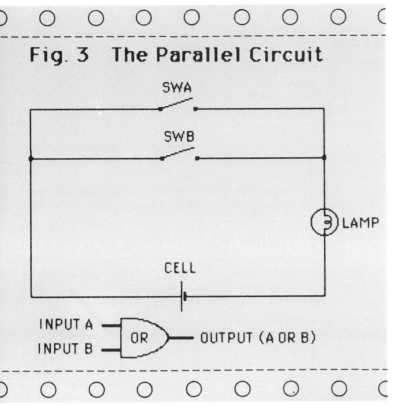

Fig. 3   The Parallel Circuit

SWA

SWB

LAMP

CELL

INPUT A — | OR | — OUTPUT (A OR B)
INPUT B —

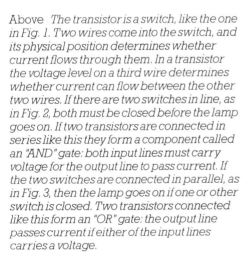

Above *The transistor is a switch, like the one in Fig. 1. Two wires come into the switch, and its physical position determines whether current flows through them. In a transistor the voltage level on a third wire determines whether current can flow between the other two wires. If there are two switches in line, as in Fig. 2, both must be closed before the lamp goes on. If two transistors are connected in series like this they form a component called an "AND" gate: both input lines must carry voltage for the output line to pass current. If the two switches are connected in parallel, as in Fig. 3, then the lamp goes on if one or other switch is closed. Two transistors connected like this form an "OR" gate: the output line passes current if either of the input lines carries a voltage.*

Right *The transistor is the essential component in microcircuitry. It may occur in its thousands as an integrated circuit (the dark rectangular components on this circuit board), or as an individual component (like the stubby metal cans on the board). Computers are really gigantic collections of simple transistor switches.*

Now let's leave those two devices for a moment and do some more binary arithmetic: specifically, we will do every single-digit binary addition that it's possible to do:

Digit A	0	0	1	1
Digit B	+0	+1	+0	+1
Answer	0	1	1	10

This makes for very simple addition rules, then:

If (A OR B is 1) AND (A AND B are not both 1)

then Answer is 1

If (A AND B are 1)

then Answer is 0 with a Carry into next column.

Now using our AND and OR gates we can turn these two rules into a circuit (provided that we can build a NOT gate, a device that turns a 5V input into a 0V output and vice versa: well we can, so let's not bother about how it works).

So, using very simple circuitry, we can build a circuit that will accept patterns of voltages representing numbers, and produce patterns of voltages representing the sum of the numbers represented. So we have built a calculator. The other rules of arithmetic can be simulated by using the Adder: Subtraction is just the Addition of a negative number; Multiplication is repeated Addition; and Division is repeated Subtraction. This circuit is called a Half Adder. We can put two single binary digits into it and get out their sum, and a carry. Remember that the digits that we are talking about are just voltage levels on a piece of wire. Now let's connect up some Half Adders to make a Full Adder that will answer sums like this:

1101	1011	1111
+1010	+1110	+1111
10111	11001	11110

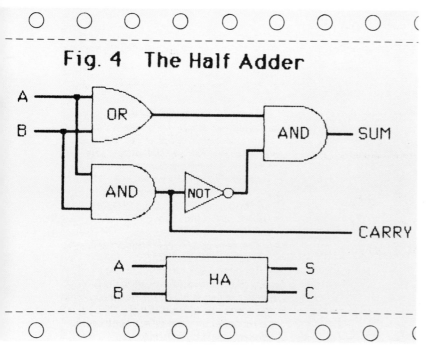

Fig. 4 The Half Adder

The Full Adder works exactly the way you do when doing sums like this: starting with the rightmost column, add up the digits in a column, add any carry digit to the answer, write the answer in this column and the carry digit (if any) in the next column. And so on.

Now all that's needed to complete the calculator is some control circuitry to ensure that numbers can be entered from the keyboard in some way, stored in the memory banks, and moved around the system from Memory to Arithmetic Unit to Memory to Output, and so on.

What remains now to turn the calculator into a computer is the ability to store a sequence of instructions in it, and have the CPU execute them in sequence. This is exactly what the CPU does: it will perform certain switching operations according to the numbers that are input to it. If we store a sequence of these operation code numbers somewhere in memory, and arrange for the CPU to execute each of these operation codes in turn until finished, then we have a stored-program computer. Finito.

Processing text, and drawing pictures on a screen is just a matter of processing numbers according to different rules, and displaying them as letters or colored dots; that may sound like evading the issue, but really the main components of a computer system are the ability to store and add numbers, and the ability to store and execute sequences of operations — everything else is a combination of coding and video circuitry.

You may have noticed in the description of the addition sequence above, that the description itself was actually a program — a series of instructions to be executed in sequence until finished. Let's look at it again:

1 Start with the rightmost column

2 Add up the digits in the current column

3 Add any carry digit to the answer

4 Write the answer in this column

5 Write the carry digit (if any) into the next column

6 If any columns remain, repeat from Step 2

7 Otherwise, Finish

For a four-digit addition, then, this sequence of operations is executed in this order:

1 23456 23456 23456 234567

Not only is this an example of a program, it's even got a test and a loop in it — the test at Step 6 sends execution back to Step 2 or onwards to Step 7.

All computer programs are of this form. They may be written in some language other than English, they may have more complex structures, but the essentials remain the same.

Now the usual input to a computer is command words or data typed in by the user at the keyboard, and the usual output is words or numbers or pictures displayed on a VDU screen. In the case of a robot, the input is more likely to be data about the outside world sent automatically from the robot's sensors, and the output is likely to be positioning commands to the robot's actuators. This hardly changes the operation of the computer, it just means that other devices replace the keyboard and the screen; the CPU and other components continue to process numbers, and switch patterns of voltage around the system.

What's missing from this picture of the robot now, given the computer, the structure, and the actuators, is the real breath of life, the software. That's another of those cant words: it just means computer programs. A robot program would have to be written in the first place by a human programer and stored in the computer. It might look something like this:

1 Send zero position commands to all actuators

2 Switch on all sensors

3 REPEAT FOLLOWING STEPS

4 Increase shoulder angle by 2 degrees

5 Increase elbow angle by 2 degrees

6 Decrease wrist angle by 1 degree

7 UNTIL END EFFECTOR COLLISION SWITCH GOES ON

8 Open gripper

9 Switch off collision switch

10 REPEAT FOLLOWING STEPS

11 Close gripper by 1 degree

12 UNTIL GRIPPER TOUCH SENSOR GOES ON

13 Send zero position commands to all actuators except gripper

14 Finish

This would send a simple arm to its zero position, then move it along a known path until the tip of its end effector hit something and closed a switch, then close its gripper

gradually until it met some resistance, then return to the zero position. It just might result in the arm going somewhere, picking it up, and bringing it back. It might.

If you imagine the circumstances of the robot for which this program is supposedly written, and you try to rewrite the program to make good its obvious deficiencies, you'll get a very clear appreciation of the limitations of robot intelligence, and the difficulties of making sense of the outside world. Some of the faults are:

1 Suppose the arm gets trapped by something on its original return to zero? How could the program detect this, and what could it do?

2 Suppose the end effector collision switch never actually goes on — because it never hits anything, or because it just brushes the object — what will happen, and what can be put into the program to detect and allow for this?

3 Suppose the gripper encounters something that it can't move — its own base, for example — what will happen, and how could the program allow for this?

4 The gripper might crush the object before its touch sensor switched on, or the touch sensor might go on before the gripper had really got a hold on the object. How could this be allowed for?

For a practical experience of these and thousands of other difficulties, try going out of the room while a friend rearranges the furniture and puts on a blindfold. Your task is to direct him or her across the room to pick up some object and bring it back. You can't see into the room, you can only give commands like "forward one pace", "left 20 degrees", "arm up 2ft", "open hand fully". Your blindfolded friend has to act as dumb as possible, and can only give you information like "my foot won't move", "my arm's hit something", "I've fallen over".

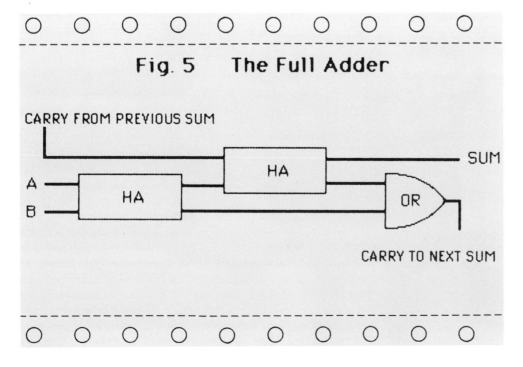

Fig. 5   The Full Adder

CARRY FROM PREVIOUS SUM

A

B

HA

HA

OR

SUM

CARRY TO NEXT SUM

Opposite *The logical rule for adding two binary digits, A and B, is "THE SUM IS ONE IF (A OR B IS ONE) AND (A AND B ARE NOT BOTH ONE). This logical statement translates into the logic circuit of Fig. 4. Two input lines carry voltage or not, the sum output line passes current or not according to the rule; it represents the sum of the two digits. The second output line indicates whether there should be a carry out from the process. This circuit is called a Half Adder.*

Left *Connecting two Half Adders as shown in Fig. 5 makes the Full Adder. If there is one Full Adder circuit for each pair of input binary digits in an addition, then the binary digits of their sum will be represented by the voltage levels on the output lines. The Adder is the essential component in a computer's Arithmetic and Logic Unit (ALU).*

1958

← - - - 7/16 in. - - - →

Left *Production standards have moved on from the pioneering days of 1958, when Jack Kilby invented the IC (integrated circuit) at Texas Instruments, USA.*

Below *Gold connection inlays form an Aztec pattern around the tiny logic circuitry at the heart of this enormously magnified modern IC. Gold is used for the connectors because of its electrical properties and resistance to corrosion.*

Left *The pure silicon into which the IC's logic circuits are etched in metal is produced as single crystals 6in in diameter and several feet long. These crystals are then thinly sliced like sausage to produce the wafers on which the chips themselves will be made — dozens of chips per wafer.*

Below *Testing and connecting these tiny circuits is delicate work — human operators use microscopes and remote controlled probes and soldering irons; this sort of intense, demanding, precision work might be done by robots one day.*

Bottom *At all stages of chip production there must be conditions cleaner and more controlled than many hospital operating theaters, in order that contamination of the chips be minimized.*

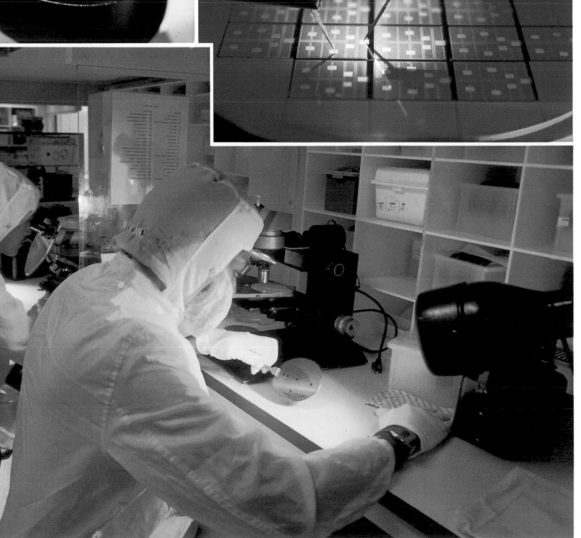

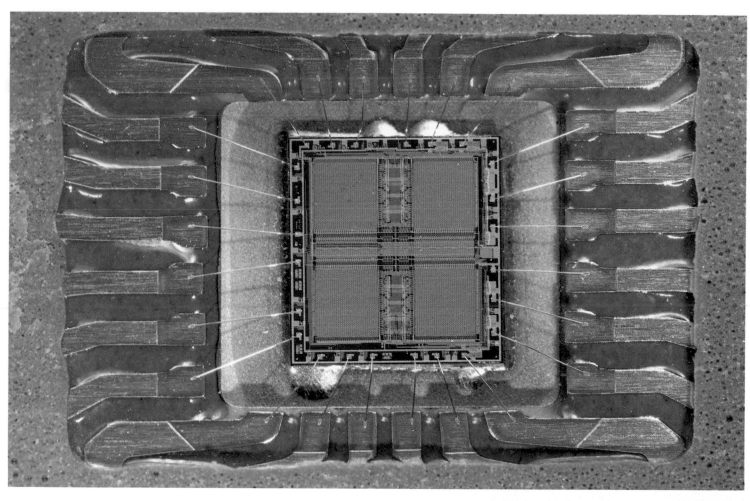

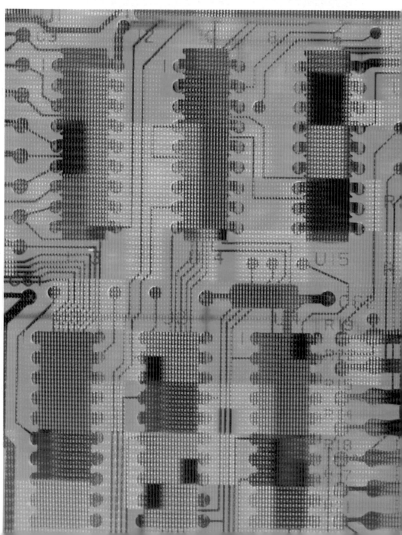

Above *The intricate detail and unmatched precision of microchip design and production have required the invention of an enormous industrial base, supplying new techniques and new materials. These are the so-called "sun-rise" industries, a truly fantastic concentration of high technology, strategic resources and very serious money.*

Right *Symbolic logic is expressed in material form in the integrated circuit: distillate of imagination and knowledge. The patterns are dictated partly by the need to arrange components as closely together as possible, and partly by the regular symmetrical nature of the logic. So fast are these devices that time taken by current to pass from one part of the circuit to another can affect the chip's operation; current travels at 186,000 miles per second — seven times around the world in a heartbeat.*

Opposite *Designing computer circuitry requires the use of computers: partly to act as electronic drawing boards, partly to provide libraries of stored designs and component specifications, and partly to optimize the human designs — by working out the best way to arrange hundreds of components so that their connections don't cross and are as short as possible, for example.*

You will immediately see how vital sensors are to make a robot do anything useful, how many sensors you'd like to have available, how maddening it is that robots can't recognize common objects, and so on. If you try to create a program from your experience of guiding your robot friend, you'll see how difficult it is to anticipate and allow for every event, and how putting more sensors and more complex actuators on your robot make the programing harder and more complicated. To complete your experience, try being the blindfolded one while your friend tries to steer you, following your program. You'll probably take a rueful pleasure in being as dumb and as literal as possible, thus making the program fail almost immediately.

We take for granted our ability to move around the real world, going places we've never been, recognizing objects we have never seen, dealing with circumstances we have never encountered before. We do these miraculous things partly because we've had a lifetime of learning, and partly because we are marvelously adept at sensing the environment, interpreting our sense data, comparing present data with millions of previous encounters, adding any new data to our existing stock of sense data, testing our hypotheses about the environment and constantly changing the behavioral rules by which we act upon our interpretations of what we sense. We are aided in this by an intricate central nervous system which contains all sorts of feedback and reflex action loops, freeing the brain from huge chunks of responsibility for the body's actions. Our brains are intelligent in marvelous ways – we can sleep through a thunderstorm but be woken by a baby's sigh; we can recognize people by their walks; we can hear two notes of a tune and remember every detail of the occasion when first we heard it. Our memories store enormous amounts of information – often unknown to us – so that we can access it all almost immediately; how else would we be able to recognize faces, or scents, or the feel of a pair of shoes?

Making robots even begin to emulate these marvels is a daunting task, and depends totally on the programer's ability to collate the incoming sense data from all sensors, compare it with stored data, store the new data in some compact but accessible form, and make actionable hypotheses about the environment from incomplete data and knowledge. So what are the sensors that robots use, and how do they work?

Touch Sensors

There are three aspects to touch sensing: proximity, contact, and pressure. Proximity sensors detect the nearness of an object without actually touching it. They can work by measuring the local air pressure very accurately so that they register the difference when moved close to some object – our skin and ears do this, giving us a "feel" for our surroundings. They can use radio or radar or optical methods of distance sensing.

Contact sensors register contact with an object, and are either on or off. In the simplest form they are just switches, closed by coming into contact with an object. The lighter the switch force, the more sensitive the touch sensing.

Pressure sensors measure the strength of a contact rather than simply its presence or absence. They commonly use the piezo-electric properties of certain crystals, which produce an

Previous pages *This is how computers should look, modern temples of the electronic soul. Today's reality is much more prosaic; desktop computers look like and are home entertainment systems; large main-frame computers resemble collections of filing-cabinets.*

Opposite top *Vision is an enormously useful sense, and roboticists are constantly trying to improve robots' ways of seeing. In this experimental system, a laser scans a surface, building a picture of its outlines from the interference of the light beam.*

Opposite bottom *The robot eye must process its data somehow; objects may be represented as mathematical relationships between points in 3D geometries.*

Below *The ability to acquire sense data about its environment is essential to a robot's control of its own actions. Hearing, vision, smell, touch and taste can all be simulated in robots; the problems lie in processing the input data into a meaningful logical "picture" of the world.*

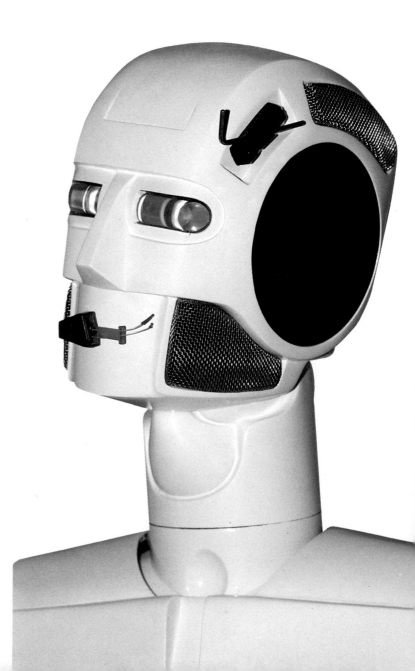

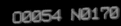

00054 N0170

GRAPH	
X	−0.0716
Y	−2.9334
Z	2.1727
F	0.45
S	1234
T	0

1.6

(FUNC-TION)	START AUTO	START	*STOP	*CONT. SINGL	ERASE	SHIFT	ENLAR-GE	GRAPH PARAM	(NEXT)

electrical current in response to external pressure; the greater the pressure, the greater the current produced. Such crystals produce the ignition spark in most modern cigarette lighters.

The choice of sensor depends upon the application. Cheap, simple sensors give low-grade information but at little cost in money or in processor time; complex sensors are expensive in money, processing time, and often current — not a negligible consideration in an autonomous robot.

Touch data is difficult to interpret alone, and is usually combined with at least one other sense for useful effect. The most striking application is surely the robot sheep shearer, developed at the University of Western Australia. Its touch sensors enable it to move the cutting head of its end effector accurately over the sheep's skin, maintaining appropriate contact and avoiding sensitive areas.

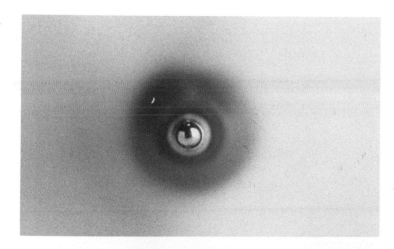

Sight Sensors

Sight is the human's most important single sense — ignoring the ability to hear speech as not precisely a sense — and we are expert at processing the enormous amounts of visual data that we constantly receive. Mimicking this sort of sensing by computer methods is difficult and requires large amounts of computer memory and processing power; in the present state of the art robots cannot be built economically with powerful vision systems on board. Much can be achieved with simple light sensors, which are, in fact, transistors that are switched by the presence or absence of light. Grey Walter's "Electronic Tortoises", built in the 1940s, used light sensors to locate their "hutches". Robots can use infra-red light sensors just as effectively, with the advantage that infra-red light passes through smoke and haze better than visible light does, and can be used for "seeing in the dark". Furthermore, such sensors can be used to detect, and thus to identify, the characteristic heat radiation patterns of surfaces — a face gives off heat in a completely different way than a soup plate, for example.

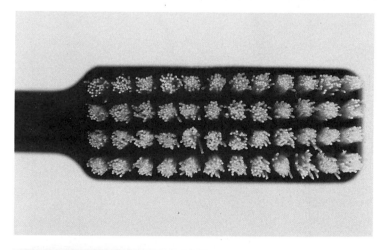

Computer scientists have developed effective pattern-recognition techniques which enable robots to identify shapes, when input to the robot's computer, such as simple silhouette pictures from a video camera. An arm equipped with such a system can work at an assembly line, putting things together, packing and unpacking, checking tolerances, sorting for size — the first robotic patent application was made in the USA in 1954 by George C. Devol for "Programed Article Transfer", which is exactly what much assembly- and production-line work involves.

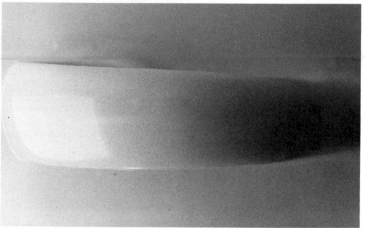

Sound Sensors

Robots that understand speech have enormous advantages for anyone building or operating them. Speech recognition systems do exist, but are, as yet, subject to certain limitations. The first is common to all sensory input: that the mass of data involved in a typical input needs time and power and specialized equipment if it is to be processed quickly enough for conversation or execution. Words spoken into a microphone, for example, are input to the computer as strings of numbers representing the frequency patterns of the sound waves; the computer has to match that pattern against stored word patterns. This takes time, and cannot be exact — when a New Yorker and a Scot say "Time", they are saying the same

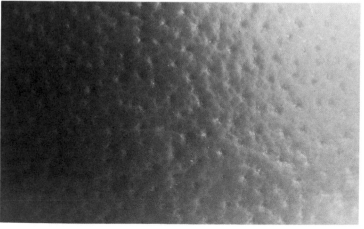

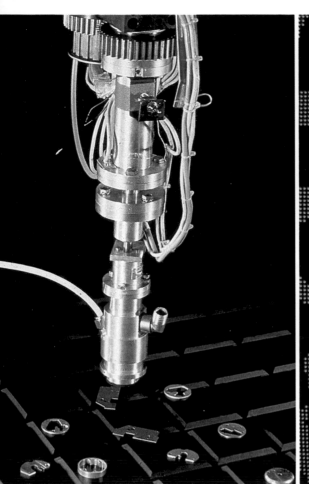

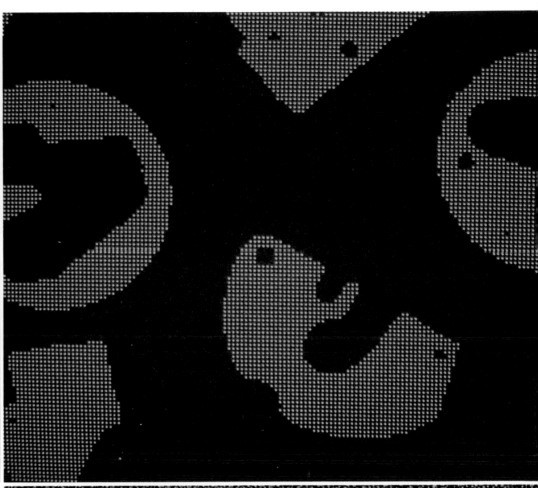

Above, top and right *The camera of this industrial vision system examines components on the assembly line. It produces standard-size silhouettes in digital form for the computer to process; these relatively simple images can be compared and measured by the computer to determine components' identity, tolerances, orientation, and so on. By reducing the information input, and by specializing the information context, this vision system achieves high recognition success: generality is traded off against precision.*

Left *When we look at objects we are aided by a lifetime's experience of seeing: the nearness, illumination and attitude of the objects are the context in which shapes of things are seen. When we are deprived of this context, our eyes see the same pictures but our brains fail to understand them: did you recognize a toothbrush, some orange peel, a cup handle, and the tip of a ball-point pen here? Imagine this effect magnified thousands of times in the case of robot vision.*

word, but is it really the same sound? Voices vary enormously from person to person and according to circumstances. Speech recognition systems, therefore, either recognize only a set number of pre-programed words for all speakers, or will continually learn new words, but only from one or a few speakers. These are not major drawbacks, but they mean that robots will generally use speech sensing to receive commands from humans, rather than as a way of exploring the world autonomously.

Other Sensors

Robots can sense smells by analyzing the chemicals in the air around them. On the Austin-Rover car production line in England, parts of the car body are filled with gas and then "sniffed" by a robot. Detection of the gas in the atmosphere points to a leak, and therefore probably a bad weld. Similar sniffers, mounted on powered carts, run along inside oil and gas pipelines checking the welds. Sniffers can detect the presence of smoke by passing air samples through a beam of light and constantly monitoring the transmission intensity. Robot security patrols in offices and factories are equipped with fire and flood detection equipment, and that could be said to involve the senses of taste and smell.

Temperature sensors can give useful information, and could be instrumental in performing a robot's task. A robot steelworker, for example, would certainly be equipped with heat sensors and thermocouples for detecting heat sources and measuring their temperature.

A Manhattan hamburger joint plans to employ a $100,000 six-armed robot cook by Christmas 1985. The robot, it is claimed, will detect and discard burnt burgers, mop up spills on tables, make change, and take orders such as "Hold the relish." In idle moments it will sing cheerful songs, and discourage vandals.

Making Sense Of It All

Sensing things is not difficult, but processing the data can be. Making sense of the real world, rather than some artificially predictable environment such as a workplace, requires clever programing and powerful computers. The cost of computing power and memory, and their physical size diminish steadily, so autonomous robots are able to carry and afford more and more sensing ability. At the same time, computer scientists all over the world involved in artificial intelligence research are producing programs that enable computers to learn about the real world — or aspects of it. "Expert systems" are programs that interrogate humans to acquire a knowledge base — for example, about all the different ways of recognizing diseases from patients' descriptions of them — and then build understanding on to that base by learning from experience.

The ability to build knowledge-understanding maps for itself is an important part of the autonomous robot's specification. As we have seen, knowledge is easily acquired, but understanding requires the collation of input data from several sensors, followed by cross-checking with stored information, and the testing of hypotheses against events. This is the problem at the heart of all information processing. It is well illustrated in the robot table-tennis competition in London in 1985, in which entrants had to construct a robot that can receive a serve and hit the ball back over the net — on a table

measuring 6½ft x 20in. The robot was required to sense the position of the ball in flight, make predictions about its flight path, and move its paddle into position for the stroke. Once the robot has been taught how to do this, long rallies will no doubt occur between competing robots, in which case the constructors may need to develop play-analysis programs, and stroke-play software. The importance of sense-data integration to understanding was demonstrated in some psychological tests in which good table tennis players were deprived of their hearing while playing: their ability to position the paddle for the return suffered from the lack of information about the speed and direction and spin of the ball which the sound of its impact on the opponent's paddle gives. Plainly, sight gives plenty of information about all these quantities, but the addition of the sound data adds a vital cross-check. Acquiring data we can do immediately; understanding it takes a little longer.

Right *The costly advanced technology of today is the home enthusiast's budget kit of tomorrow. This all-British vision system comprises the Beasty arm, two servomotors and Beasty controller, the Event One Snap Camera, and a BBC microcomputer.*

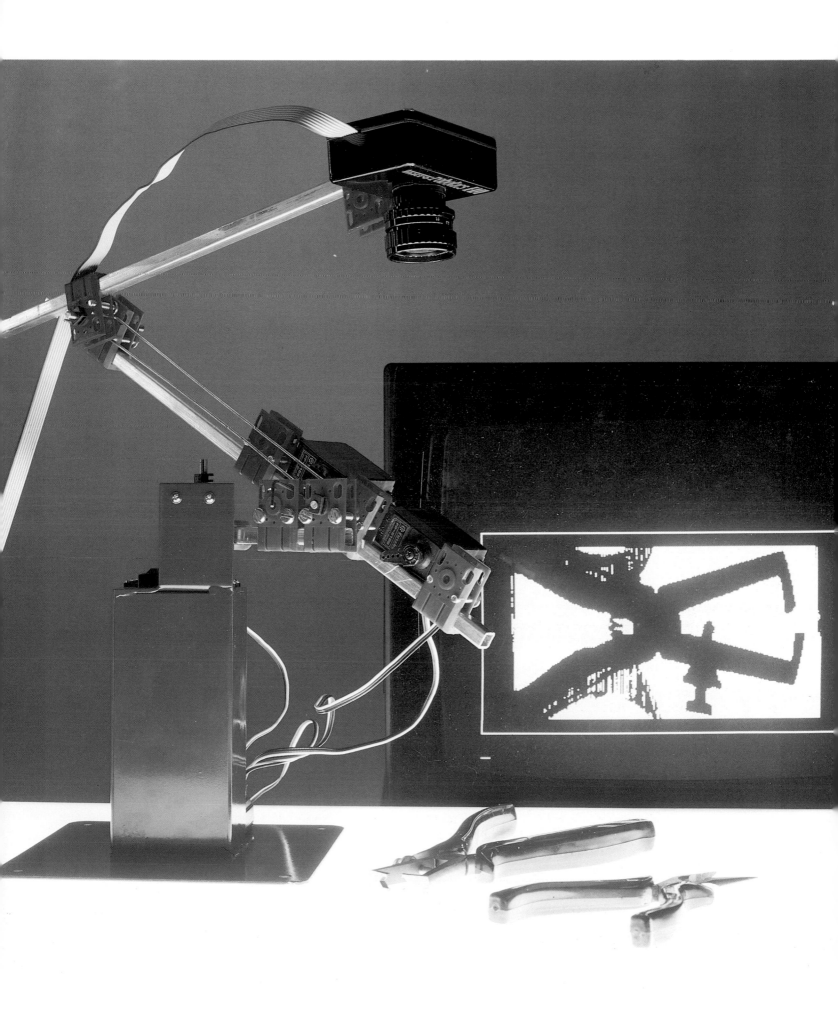

Robots in Industry

*"I like work: it fascinates me.
I can sit and look at it for hours.
I love to keep it by me:
the idea of getting rid of it nearly breaks my heart."*
Three Men In A Boat — *Jerome K. Jerome*

As robots have moved out of the computing laboratories and into factories in particular and the world of work in general, their roles as workers have started to emerge in several clear-cut forms. These roles have been arrived at through the interaction of employers' expectations, robots' capabilities, and roboticists' imagination and sales drive. Naturally, the interaction has not been without friction, but more light than heat seems to have been generated, so that in a field noted for the diversity of its opinions and the evanescence of its definitions, there is emerging a notable degree of consensus on the useful employment of robots as one additional factor among many in the productive process.

One of the most influential voices in the industrial robot field throughout its history is that of Joseph Engelberger, President of Unimation Inc., founded by Engelberger in 1961, and the first US company concerned solely with robotics. "With robotics," says Engelberger, "you'll have a steady and continuing decline in blue collar workers. For 25 years they'll largely be replaced by knowledge workers. Knowledge workers are those whose human adaptability and brain power are essential, and more economic, and wiser things to use than the limited amount of brainpower you get with a robot." That view is amplified by the words of a relative newcomer to the field, Phillipe Villers, President and founder in 1980 of Automatix, a new kind of robot company: "We wish to become the leader in a field that has not hitherto existed...robotics systems. That is, taking the robots, the computers, the software, the advanced senses such as vision, and putting them all together for the customer; a function that users presently have to perform for themselves."

Villers goes on to categorize the past and present states of robotics: "The first wave of robotics is essentially powerful material movers, dumb brutes carrying heavy loads in very adverse environments. Second wave robots, which are really just arriving, are generally lightweight, nimble and intelligent. Intelligent in two ways: first, they can adapt themselves in certain ways to their environment because of advanced senses such as vision...The other increase in robotic intelligence is computing power that's able to make use of what the senses

say, to adapt to whatever the task is. And that's basically what the second wave robots are: intelligent robots with advanced sensors and more intelligent computers."

Presumably Villers feels that the third wave of robots — faster, stronger, equipped with more sensors, better able through more intelligent software to cope with a wider range of more complex tasks — will be the complete labor force, the metal collar workers, for the industrialist's dream — total automation, zero personnel?

"The automated factory that people talk about," says Villers, "is much like the Holy Grail — something you keep on approaching and searching for and never quite reach...But what are you looking to replace? People who are being used as robots — that's all that robots are able to do." Which accords with Engelberger's view of the robot's entry to the workplace: "Robots enter the work force rather gently...Of our 3,000 robots I don't know of anywhere someone could say, 'Hey! That robot took my job!'...The way to displace labor so you don't have a crisis is to do it at the normal attrition rate. The attrition rate in metalworking in the United States is about 16 per cent a year...So you put robots in a job that either didn't exist, or you put them in jobs that retirees leave, or you put them in jobs that are so miserable that people don't want them."

For all his pioneering history in a hi-tech industry wreathed about with romantic myths and sci-fi legends, Engelberger has a clear image of robotics as part of the historic progression of mainstream manufacturing industry: "I look to robotics as another form of automation, a way to revolutionize manufacturing. You know, 47 per cent of the labor force was in farming in 1870; by 1970 only 4 per cent of the labor force was in farming. So in a hundred-year period the entire picture has completely changed. It gave this country tremendous strength."

Opposite   The essential industrial robotic qualities are clearly seen in this powerful squid-like manipulator at the Northrop Corporation, USA. Power and strength are expressed in its form, versatility in its use of suction-pad end effectors for lifting fragile sheets of graphite material, and programability in the operator's use of the teach pendant.

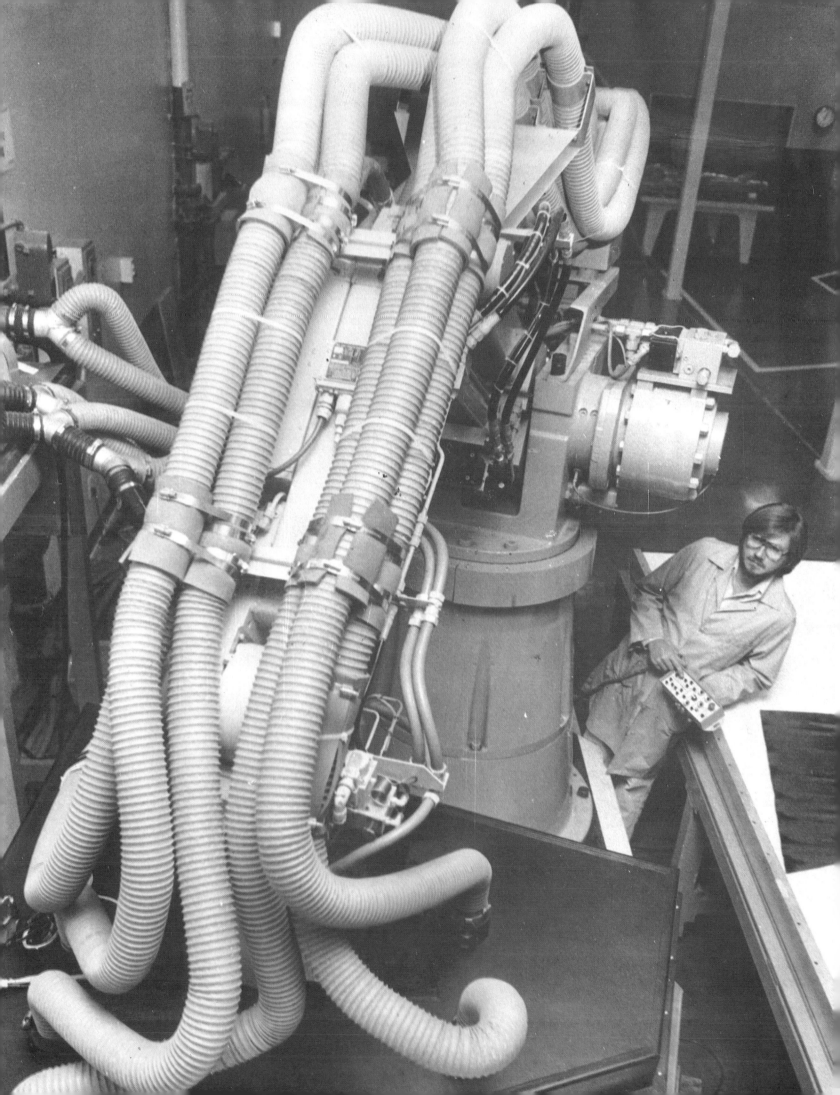

Opposite *Industrial assembly lines have never been pleasant places for human workers, being noisy, monotonous, dangerous and alienating; this robot assembly line with no human in sight seems to throb with the clangorous energy of Vulcan's forge or Hephaestus' smithy.*

Opposite bottom *The clean functionality of the welding end effector shows that, in the robot aesthetic, form is the emergent of function.*

Right *Caulking seams on an auto production line is smelly tiring work. The Cincinnati Milacron arm, equipped with glue-gun, requires few joints and relatively little power to cope with the demands of the line. Its position sensors enable it to adjust its pace to that of the work.*

American and Japanese labor unions have been largely in agreement with these views while Viller's first robotic wave has lapped gently at the factory doors. This began to happen in Japan coincidentally with a disproportionate rise in labor costs, reflected in sagging productivity; both unions and management saw the introduction of low-grade, material-shifting robots as likely to improve productivity in straightforward increased throughput. Significantly, it improved labor force morale and productivity by releasing human workers from the arduous, dirty tasks of production which few people would choose to do, and which even fewer are capable of doing efficiently for a full shift. The Japanese attitude to changes in employment patterns has always been to use increased productivity to pay for seemingly surplus workers who might, in other countries, be seen as soaking up the economic gains from that increase. In the light of forty years of world-beating industrial performance from the Japanese it is hard for European and North American observers to claim that the Japanese approach is perverse or wrong-headed, no matter how blatantly it seems to fly in the face of conventional western management wisdom. It remains to be seen whether the productivity gains from the second and third waves of robots will be sufficiently rewarding for the Japanese to maintain their consensus, as the jobs taken on by new robots are less often only the unskilled, routine and hazardous.

The Japanese unions' attitude found an echo in US labor's minds for the same reasons of human employee welfare, and the dawning knowledge that US productivity and export trade success must be won against increasing Japanese competition – anything that improved productivity was good for employment security. The second wave looks set to change that view, as Irving Bluestone, Vice President of the United Auto Workers indicated in 1979: "The introduction of automation will be so rapid in the next 5 to 15 years that it will mean the kind of job displacements we must pay attention to in an ever more effective way... A robot today costs about $20,000; that's less than what it costs to have one employee on the assembly line for one year. With such a low cost, you can anticipate the kinds of investments that will be made in GM, Ford, Chrysler and the independents to bring robots and computerized equipment into the plants." It is poignant in the light of these words to note that Unimation's historic first robot was sold in 1961 to the Ford Motor Company; more significantly, Ford to this day refer to robots as "universal transfer devices", the name they coined in 1961 as an acceptable euphemism for what they saw as the disturbing word, robot.

Perhaps the last word here should be left to one of the first speakers on the whole subject – George C. Devol, who coined the term "universal automation" which became "unimation", and whose 1954 robotics patent application was the first such in the US (though not the first in the world – that honor goes to a British inventor, Cyril W. Kenward, whose March 1954 UK patent application anticipated that of George Devol by a few months). Writing in 1983 he was optimistic about the future of robotics and its effects on human welfare: "As has been pointed out many times, robots, which can eliminate or minimize dangerous, dull, and repetitive industrial operations from the human workforce will have a profound influence on the way industry – and society – is structured in the coming years. For example, [it is] forecast that by 1995 worker injuries in factories will be reduced by up to 41 per cent, as a 'result of robot installations'...I believe that there are better things for humankind to do than to be robots themselves. It is a horrible concept to conceive of a man keeping up with a machine. But if we plan wisely, we can utilize these machines to put our nation back on the productivity track and leave to posterity a world, which, although highly industrialized, will be far more pleasant a place to live and work in than it has ever been."

Arduous, Hazardous And Dirty

Outside of the factories the industrial conditions most
unpleasant for human workers are underground, under the sea,
in nuclear and chemical plants, and on the battlefield. Robots
and robotic devices are used increasingly widely, partly for
humanitarian reasons and partly because employing the
robot does not entail the high costs of protecting and
sustaining human lives in dangerous conditions.

Coal mining has long been extensively mechanized, and
the introduction of robot technology is just the last ingredient
in the first stages of complete automation. With the intelligent
control of action and sensory systems that robots are
increasingly able to provide, the stage is set for underground
operations to become far more an interactive production
system, rather than a more or less conventionally organized
raw materials process that happens to occur underground —
conducted by machine under human supervision and
direction. Robot technology, for example, can synchronize the
work of the giant coal-face cutting machines with the actions of
the conveyor belts and trucks that carry the coal away, while
advancing the hydraulic roof supports behind the cutters, and
monitoring the quality of coal and likely future directions of the
seam. The recent developments in sniffing and tasting sensors
generally have built on mining research into the detection of
dangerous gasses and water penetration underground.

Less far underground than the mines but equally distasteful
to humans are the sewers, tunnels and cableways beneath our
cities. Tracked robot vehicles — as yet remotely controlled via
television cameras and umbilical control cables — are in use

cleaning and inspecting sewers, drains and pipes. With the
growth in recent years of continental grids of oil and gas
pipelines, this last may well become the most significant
application. In Britain plans are being made to create a national
grid of optical-fiber cable for TV and telecommunications
transmissions. Robot vehicles will certainly be used for much
of this work, and it has been suggested that they may drag the
cables along the sewers, fixing them in position with the aid of
a drill and glue gun.

The British telephone company, British Telecom
International, has had extensive experience of cable-laying
operations in all conditions, and has an undersea cable-laying
robot constantly employed around the world. Called Seadog,
and built on the chassis of a light battle tank, this large tracked
vehicle (again remotely controlled from the support ship
carrying the cable itself and monitoring systems) can swim
underwater and on the surface, or crawl along the seabed.
There, it ploughs a trench, places the cable, and backfills as it
moves. It can also locate existing cables and repair them or
pass them to the surface, saving the company years of time
wasted on expensively dragging the seabed with grapnels in
the search for otherwise inaccessible damaged lines.

Britain's oil industry in its drilling work under the North
Sea has made extensive use of remote-controlled and free-
swimming submersibles for inspection and routine
maintenance of offshore platforms, seabed pipelines and
well-heads. One of the significant economic (rather than
humanitarian) costs of using human divers for this kind of
work, is their need to spend long periods of time working

Left *Looking like a military gravedigger or an agricultural battle tank, the KGH Remote-Controlled Manipulator Vehicle was an early West German response to the problems of maintenance and repair in nuclear installations.*

Right *Hazard has long been the mother of invention in the specialized field of nuclear power station robots. "Rivet", built for damage-control and inspection at Britain's Harwell Atomic Energy plant in 1967, is the forerunner of the vastly more powerful "Herman", which stood ready for use during the 1979 "China Syndrome" accident at Three Mile Island, USA.*

Below *The need to handle radioactive material delicately at a distance stimulated the science of telechirics. The operator is safe behind several feet of glass, but his movements of the control arms are repeated by the flexible telechirs in the "hot zone".*

from expensive pressurized accommodation, and sometimes equally long periods of idleness in decompression chambers returning to normal conditions. Robots, of course, are not subject to pressure trauma, nor do they need the enormous life-support systems required to keep commercial divers working economically at depth.

General Electric's Diver Equivalent Manipulator System (DEMS) is intended to participate in the search for undersea reserves, and is a diving bell equipped with a robot arm. It can drill, cut cable, retrieve debris and help in rescue work. Shipboard operators "fly" DEMS by remote control, and manipulate the arm by moving a master control arm whose actions are mimicked by the DEMS arm underwater. Television cameras complete the esential feedback loop.

The US Navy took an early interest in these submersibles, and will commission modified versions in 1985. Built to Navy specifications by Honeywell's Defense Systems division, they are "mine neutralization systems" for use by mine-sweeping surface craft. When a mine is located by conventional methods, the robot submersible swims to it under the guidance of its own and the mother ship's sonar (an interesting addition to the range of robot senses). It then severs the mine's moorings, allowing it to float to the surface, or – depending upon what it observes of the mine's type and state – can explode it *in situ.*

Submersibles have been developed in Germany for the inspection of the cooling systems of nuclear power stations. The size and shape of a household trash can, the robot is driven and steered by water jets. It carries TV cameras into places which would otherwise be inaccessible because of geometry or radiation hazards.

These conditions have stimulated a British company, Taylor Hitac, to develop a range of specialized robots for use in the nuclear industry. Perhaps the most striking is the reactor demolition robot, which stands 60 ft high on hydraulic stilts. It descends into the reactor vessel and removes the radioactive graphite core, then cuts the vessel into pieces using a cutting torch and magnetic gripper. The company has equally inventive plans for the hazardous task of transporting reactor fuel pins: robot vehicles to carry them through tunnels using magnetic levitation and propulsion.

Other parts of these sites, and of chemical and explosive plants, will be patrolled by robot vehicles such as the British Morfax Marauder and the Rocomp from the Battelle Institute of Ohio. These miniature tanks follow remote directions or programed patrol paths, avoiding obstacles (climbing stairs with ease) and stopping at pre-set points to monitor radiation, collect air samples or take smears from suspect surfaces – further additions to the robot sensor collection.

A less heavy-duty version of these corridor crawlers is the Craft robot built by students at the Cranfield Institute of Technology in England. They see it as a cheap robotic messenger, able to navigate factory and office floors under its own electric power, skirting obstacles and responding to infra-red commands from the central messaging computer. It can carry loads up to 50 lbs, but being a three-wheeler is restricted to flat surfaces.

Patrol duties are attracting increasing robot application. Denning Mobile Robotics of Massachusetts has a contract to

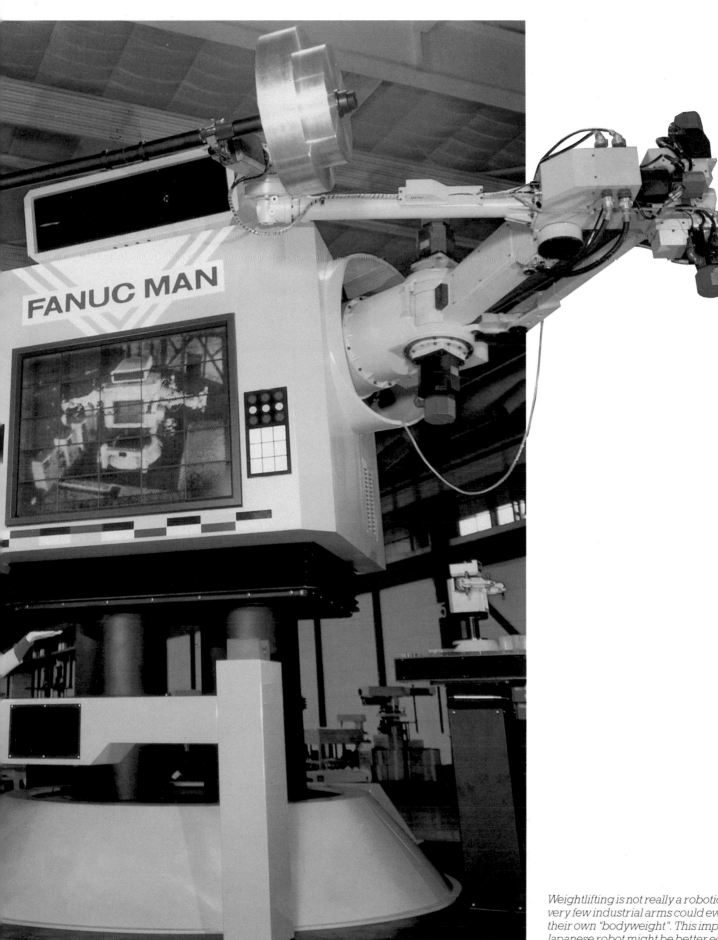

Weightlifting is not really a robotic sport, and very few industrial arms could even move their own "bodyweight". This impressive Japanese robot might be better equipped designing color co-ordinates.

supply 200 robot guards to Southern Steel of Texas. They will patrol prison corridors, using infra-red vision and ammonia-sensitive sniffers to detect humans. The US Army have experimented with robot sentries but none has been put into production.

Arms and the Man...

As we have seen in a dozen different ways, the most successful robotic application in use is the industrial manipulator — the robot arm. Both Devol's and Kenward's original patents referred to manipulators designed for pick-and-place operations, and Kenward's patent application drawing shows a two-armed manipulator with 4 degrees of freedom traveling over the workplace on a three-axis Cartesian racking system. Unimation's first arm (installed in 1961) tended a die-casting machine, supplying it with forms and workpieces and removing the finished articles; the generation of robots that it spawned entered the factories in that role, serving die-casting, injection-molding, milling and grinding machines, presses and so on. The robots picked-and-placed materials without a great deal of intelligence or

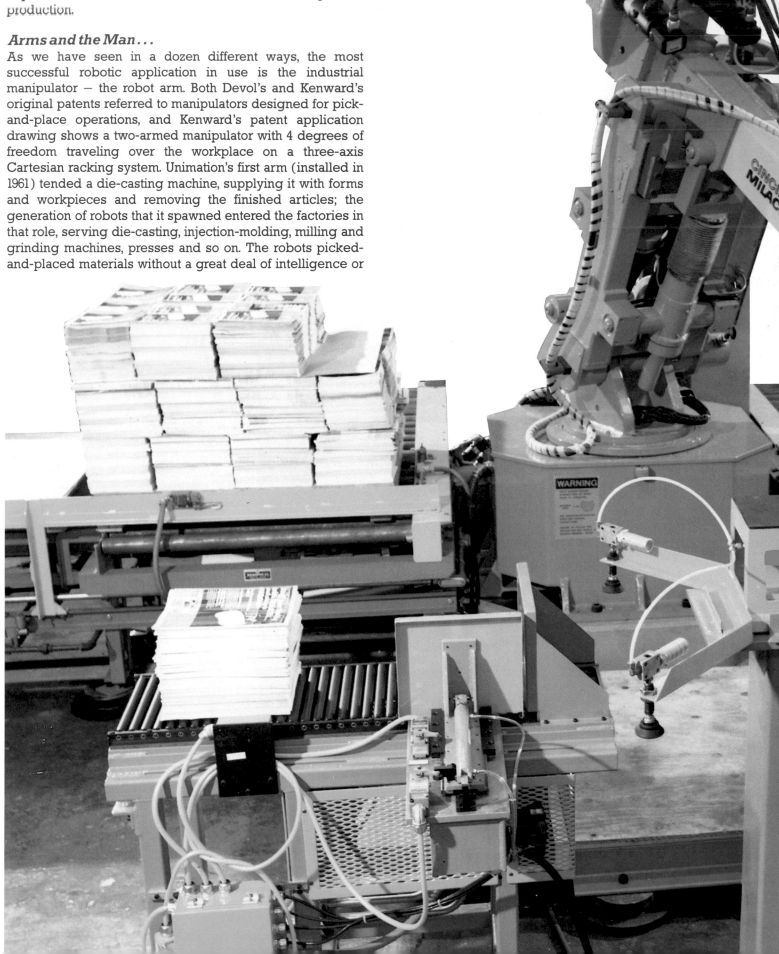

precision, but uncomplainingly, reliably, reprogramably and despite fumes, noise and danger — displaying exactly the qualities that make them so attractive as replacements for unskilled human labor.

The first processing application robot came from the Norwegian agricultural machinery company of Trallfa, and was developed in 1966 by consultant engineer Ole Molaug because it was difficult to keep human staff employed on the unpleasant task of painting wheelbarrows. By 1969 Trallfa was selling robots to other firms, and two of their first production batch are still enamelling bath tubs and shower trays for the Swedish firm that bought them.

The Unimation robots, meanwhile, had been found to be ideal for performing another unpleasant semi-skilled task — namely, spot-welding. Here, the end-effector is a gripper claw with an attached welding rod; the arm positions the rod at the weld site, closes the gripper over the spot (usually a seam between two metal panels) and strikes the arc between one claw and the other, welding the materials together in a spot about the size of a nickel. General Motors in Detroit in 1969 were the first customers for these robots, followed in 1972 by the Fiat car company. The Japanese automobile industry had been following these developments with great interest, and quickly began installing robots; the Japan Industrial Robot Association was the first such body in the world — formed in 1971, four years in advance of the US and six years ahead of the UK.

Since those pioneering days, the real advances in robot arms have been in their controllers and software, with great

Pick-and-place operations in assembly and materials handling are emerging robot specialisms. Note the baling end effector, and the hazard warning on this Cincinnati T3.

73

progress being made in sensor technology, especially vision systems. The modern Unimates and their copies are the obvious descendants of the hydraulic manipulators of the 1960s, but successful though they have been, they are outnumbered today by the Swedish ASEA robots and their look-alikes.

The ASEA IRb6, an all-electric drive arm produced in 1973, was described as the first commercial all-electric robot, even though there were some rivals available at the time. The all-electric machines now dominate arc-welding, the first such use being claimed by Kawasaki in 1974 when they installed a Kawasaki-Unimate to weld motorcycle frames. In fact, Hawker Siddeley, the British aircraft company, had been manufacturing AMF Versatran arms for some time under licence, and in 1972 adapted a Versatran for use by British Rail, the national railway organization, in welding trucks.

In 1975 a US machine-tool company, Cincinnati Milacron, produced what came to be known as the T3 robot ("The Tomorrow Tool"). Greatly improved control and software systems gave it an unmatched flexibility and precision, while its ability to monitor its own performance for error and breakdowns made it a sophisticated addition to the most advanced machine shop. It was first used mainly for drilling, tapping and milling operations in metalwork processes, especially in the US aerospace industry.

While Cincinnati Milacron were developing this market, ASEA were cornering another — metal finishing and fettling.

NUC TAPE CENTER - MODEL D

In 1976 their ASEA 60 kg robot was installed in a Swedish iron foundry where it used a pneumatic grinding wheel to finish castings. Since then grinding, reaming, blending and fettling have become major areas of robotic application — as ever, because the tasks are repetitive, dirty and arduous. The workpieces are usually weighty, requiring the robots to be large and powerful in contrast to the more lightweight models used in the precision operations of machine-tooling.

The use of robots in assembly processes was an obvious step, but had to wait until 1975, when Olivetti manufactured a multi-armed overhead gantry machine, the Sigma. It and its successors have been used for electronic component insertion and typewriter keyboard assembly.

Unimation produced in 1978 one of the best known industrial robots, to a General Motors specification for an arm with a working envelope similar to a human's, and with a load capacity of 5 lbs. This was the PUMA (Programable Universal Machine for Assembly), which has cornered many parts of the robot assembly market, partly because of its programing features, and partly through its low weight and flexibility: the PUMA series 250, for example, weighs only 15 lbs, plus 75 lbs for the controller, making just 90 lbs, compared with the typical welding assembly robot at, say, 1500 lbs. Naturally Unimation's Engelberger will be heard on the subject: "Ninety per cent of the parts in an automobile weigh less than 5 lbs — which is kind of a surprise to me; that there are all these 3,000-lb behemoths on the road, and most of them weigh less than 90 lbs. So now we had a standard. We wanted a machine that could stand in an assembly line in a space occupied by a human, and could work in an indexing line currently used by human workers, and accomplish that work at approximately the same speed. So PUMA was born." Among its current assembly tasks are the insertion of light bulbs in sockets for GM assembly lines, and the placing of chocolate candy selections in boxes for a British confectionery manufacturer.

Japanese robot manufacturers supplied Japanese and other markets without any really remarkable innovations until 1979 when the SCARA robot was developed at Yamanashi University. SCARA stands for Selective Compliance Assembly Robot Arm, embodying a concept vital to robot assembly work: the arm moves rigidly and precisely in the vertical planes, but exhibits compliance, or flexibility of positioning, in the horizontal. It can thus accurately drill, press and punch vertically, and insert screws, bolts and dies horizontally — so-called "peg-in-the-hole" operations, in which the arm aligns the object with the notional center of the hole into which it is to be inserted, but then moves it with manipulable force so that the local geometry of the hole and object themselves supply the exact positioning. This is just what humans do when locating objects, and its absence had been the gravest outstanding defect of assembly arms. The SCARA robot developed Hitachi's work with the Hi-T-Hand robot, first shown in 1974, which used force-sensitive feedback in guiding pins into holes and threading nuts and bolts. The Sankyo Scara is sold by IBM as the 7535 robot.

The modern industrial robot picture was complete by the end of the 1970s with the introduction of satisfactory, if limited, vision systems. Work began on this problem in the 1960s, teams at Scottish and North American universities being foremost. A team from Nottingham University in England, however, demonstrated the SIRCH facility in 1972; this was capable of pattern recognition under approximately industrial conditions. Cost and complexity restricted the commercial use of such systems until the end of the decade, however.

In December 1982 the Robot Institute of America found 6,250 robots at work in the US — the product of a $155 million annual market, and projected a growth of 35 per cent annually, which implies 100,000 in place by 1990. The 1982 usage was analyzed thus:

Spot Welding	1190
Arc Welding	270
Painting	290
Finishing & Fettling	30
Assembly	50
Machine load/unload	1470
Die Casting	880
Investment Casting	120
Material Handling	1950

These numbers have grown and will no doubt continue to do so, more or less in line with RIA projections.

The major steps in industrial robotics today are concerned with integrating the advances of recent years in applications,

Below *The maintenance of large modern computer systems would be impossible without the aid of their built-in diagnostic software; robotic devices are essential in the minutely detailed tasks of microchip and computer assembly; the day is not far off when robots will assemble and maintain one another. The point of real significance in this photograph, however, is that building a robot hand so that it can use a screwdriver or other tool designed for the human hand is an expensive and complicated solution — much better to clip a screwdriver bit into the wrist and make the whole arm an intelligent specialist tool for the moment.*

Above and right *The effort and ingenuity required to ape human construction with mechanical methods is evident in this experimental hand. A sense of touch is provided by the pressure sensors on the inside of the hand; they might be electrical strain gauges, or gas- or fluid-filled sacs. What is important is that the hand should be able to grip a semi-fragile object firmly enough to hold it, but not to crush it.*

hardware and software into Flexible Manufacturing Systems (FMS) which present a complete industrial package. Tailored to specific industries if need be, but essentially the all-singing, all-dancing general-purpose robot handyman, equipped with a range of end effectors and sensors, and easily programed and reprogramed for any task within its physical capabilities. The computer industry has taken forty years to appreciate that ease of use and generality are what really count with customers, but the robotics industry seems to have learned something from their experience.

Perhaps we should close this section with a story told in the largely unrobotized British automobile industry. Fiat began promoting its cars in 1982 with operatically orchestrated film of its robot car plants in Italy: "Built by robots" was the slogan; "Bought by morons" was the sour British reply, with the — possibly scurrilous — addendum that "The first 1,500 rolled off the production line with the doors beautifully welded — shut."

Action At A Distance

Many of the techniques and technology employed by roboticists in their development of robot arms came from the allied fields of teleoperations and remote control. People have always used remote control devices to extend the reach,

power and hardiness of the human limbs — the lever, of course, is the quintessential agent of "action at a distance" — but the growth in remote handling techniques really began in the metal industries, where smelting, casting and rolling large amounts of very hot metal demanded simple robust machines. Work on this machinery took on new urgency and unheard-of precision in the atomic energy programs begun during the Second World War. Here it became necessary for scientists to manipulate small quantities of extremely dangerous substances, usually at a distance, and often from behind several inches of protective glass.

The first remote manipulators, then, were simply leather or cloth gauntlets sealed into the casing of a work-vessel or chamber. These were superseded by mechanical "waldo" systems in which the movements of the operator's hands in a control set of gloves were mechanically transmitted to the slave "hands" at the workplace. These devices soon attracted the name of "telechirs" from the Greek for "hands at a distance." The precision of these devices has increased as electronics and electrical engineering techniques have improved, in part under the robot impetus. Telechirs are in constant use in nuclear plants, chemical factories, explosives plants — all the places where dangerous substances and devices have to be handled by humans at a distance.

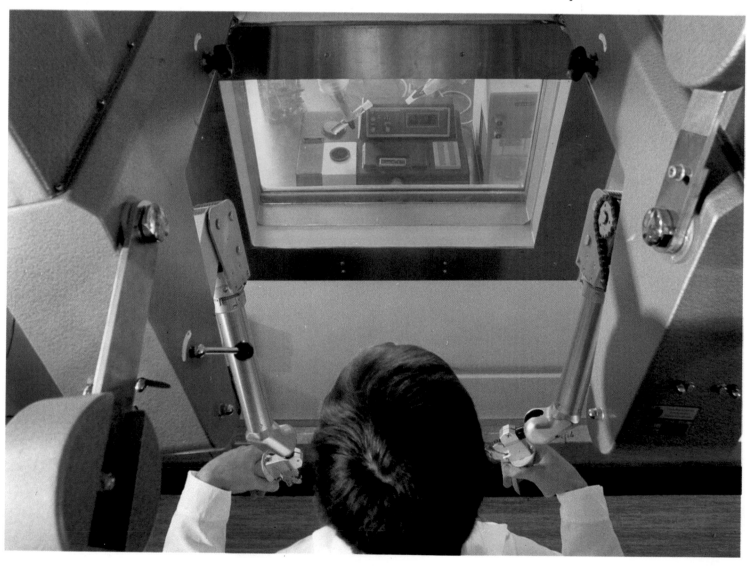

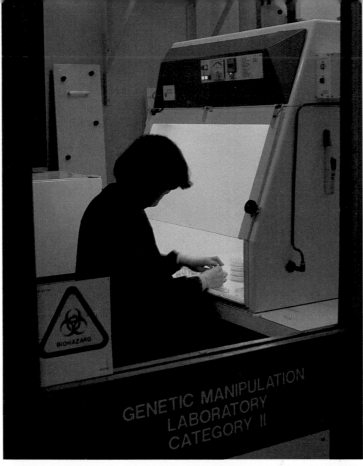

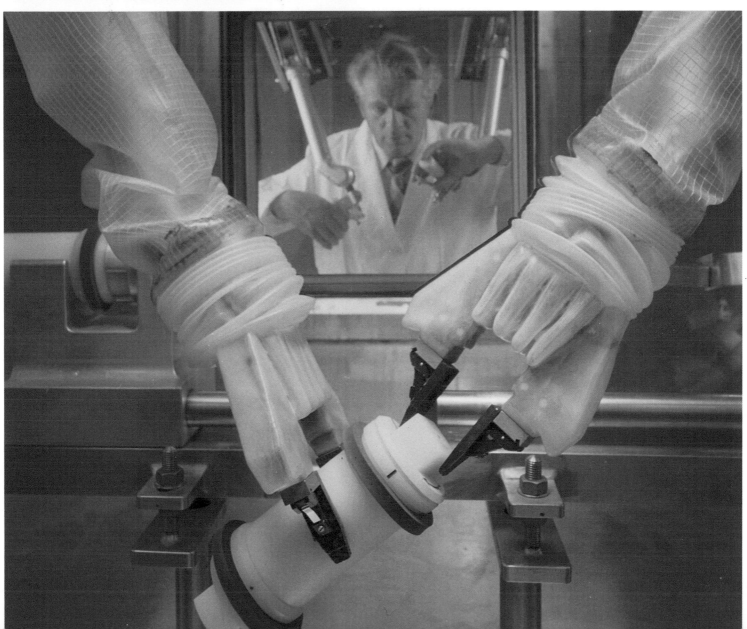

Bottom left *The task of manipulating remote objects seems much harder when seen from the operator's side of the glass. Notice how the attitudes of his hands, wrists and forearms are translated by the telechir joints.*

Left *The emerging and highly controversial field of genetic manipulation has used telechirs from the start; workers need to be isolated from possible contamination by or of their work, and are constantly engaged in microsurgery involving tiny movements under microscopic magnification. Telechirs serve both purposes.*

Bottom *The correspondence between the operator's movements and those of the "waldos" is clearly demonstrated here. Opening a screw-top container like this is a test of the operator's and the grippers' sophistication.*

Their manipulability is now such as to extend rather than merely to mimic or reproduce that of human hands: surgeons operating on the brain or inside a knee joint, scientists dissecting microscopic samples of plants and animals, technicians building and testing microchip devices all use telechirs with microscope visual feedback, allowing the operator's hand movements to be reduced from normal scale to precise fractions of an inch. A recent development in nuclear reactor equipment is a telechir comprising a chain of links ending in an end effector: this is introduced into a tube — in a cooling system, for example — and is unwound from a storage drum under the control of a technician with visual feedback from a TV until the end effector reaches the work-site — a faulty weld in the reactor-vessel casing, say — when the operator then uses it as a remote extension hand for repair and maintenance.

Whereas microscopic telechirs gear-down human movements, and necessarily reduce the forces and velocities applied, other remote action devices do the opposite, magnifying movement and amplifying force. Many automobiles, for example, have servo-assisted brakes and steering, in which the force of the human's hand or foot is amplified by hydraulic or pneumatic servo-systems. Electrically driven telechirs, however, are starting to appear which amplify human capabilities in far less prosaic applications.

The problems of feedback become acute immediately electrical telechirs are introduced: a mechanical linkage can transmit a "feel" from the work back to the operator, so that grasping forces and "give" can be sensed; similarly, power-assisted steering systems in automobiles have to be built to transmit vibration and force back from the wheels to the driver. To reproduce this feedback in electrical telechirs requires high-precision engineering to transmit accurate representations of grip-force and weight. This control is essential in telechirs, and paramount when the telechir becomes an "exoskeleton."

Imagine bringing the power-assisted hand of the typical telechir out of its remote worksite, and actually fitting it around the operator's own hand; now the human provides the control movements, but the telechir's effector contacts the load, and its power assistance does the actual work. Imagine the operator clothed in a telechir whole-body system — hands, arms, feet and legs all telechir-operated — and you

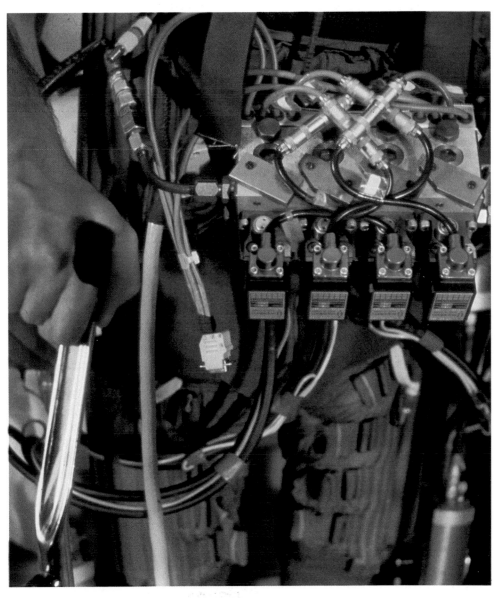

Left *Providing new power for old or wasted limbs is the aim of these hydraulic exoskeletons. The small or weak movements of the operator are amplified by the power supply. Achieving smooth repeatable control is of the essence with all mechanical feedback systems.*

Right *The "lash-up" arrangements of the experimenters reveal the complexity of their hydraulic engineering. Some details of the exoskeleton can be seen; like hockey-players' leg pads, they can be cinched tightly where needed on the body for support and control.*

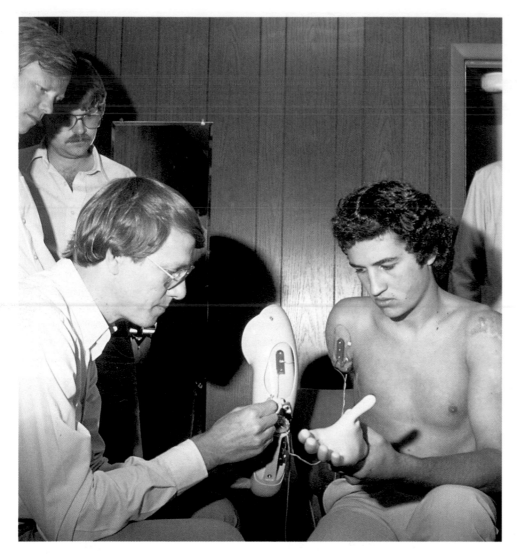

Left *Modern myo-sensing techniques allow prostheses to function almost as robot symbiotes: they take their control signals from the tiny electrical currents in the nerves and muscles remaining in the limb, and make the corresponding move under the power of their electric motors.*

Right *Slightly more up to date, this prosthesis from the University of Utah employs discrete-component electronic circuitry, but has a very rudimentary wrist and end effector.*

Right below *A more unlikely idea than the Walking Truck is hard to imagine, but one glance at the prototype reveals its real potential for load-carrying in rough terrain. The marriage of the operator's decision-making skills with the robot's mechanical abilities may yet prove to be the way of avoiding rather than solving the problem of artificial intelligence.*

have a kind of skeletal robot with a human operator inside; this is the exoskeleton. The first examples of this device were the extreme-depth diving suits developed in the 1940s and 1950s. They looked like armored two-armed Easter Eggs, and took much of their joint geometry from the suits of plate armor built in Europe in the Middle Ages; in the late 1960s NASA scientists visited European armor collections for the same inspirations while designing the first extra-vehicular space-suits.

The first applications of the exoskeleton were as aids to the disabled: supporting, amplifying, and, of course, exercising limbs wasted by congenital defects or nervous system plagues such as poliomyelitis. From this developed powered prostheses – replacement limbs such as today's Steeper Myoelectric Hand – which take control signals directly from the wearer's muscles in the undamaged part of the limb, and amplify them to operate a powered replica of the missing limb.

Very quickly industry and the military realized that this sort of technology could produce super-laborers, capable of clearing tall buildings at one bound, lifting tanks out of trenches, and straightening railway lines. Such monsters are indeed possible, and one can imagine them put to good use in many industrial applications; as ever in such systems, the most important limitation is the accuracy of the feedback and

sensing loops. The damage that a person wearing such an exoskeleton might wreak inadvertently on the environment is equalled or surpassed in its horrific significance by what such a cyborg might do to itself. The operator, therefore, needs to be able to sense the weight and inertia of the objects that it contacts, and the skeleton's control mechanism must differentiate between the operator's planned movements, requiring amplification, and his or her involuntary or personal movements, absolutely not to be amplified – such as sneezing, stumbling or slapping an insect off the end of the nose.

The most spectacular development of the exoskeleton is the Walking Truck developed by the Cybernetic Anthropomorphous Machine Systems Division of General Motors for the US Army. The operator sits in a cab with control limbs attached to his or her arms and legs, and the movements of these controls are reproduced in the four powered legs that are the truck's motive power. The advantages of this bizarre creation are its versatility, load-carrying and off-road capabilities. To the operator it apparently feels like crawling on top of a giant armadillo! The ancient Scythians, whose early prowess in action against the Greeks as light cavalry gave the Greeks their mythological beast (the half-human half-horse Centaur), would no doubt approve.

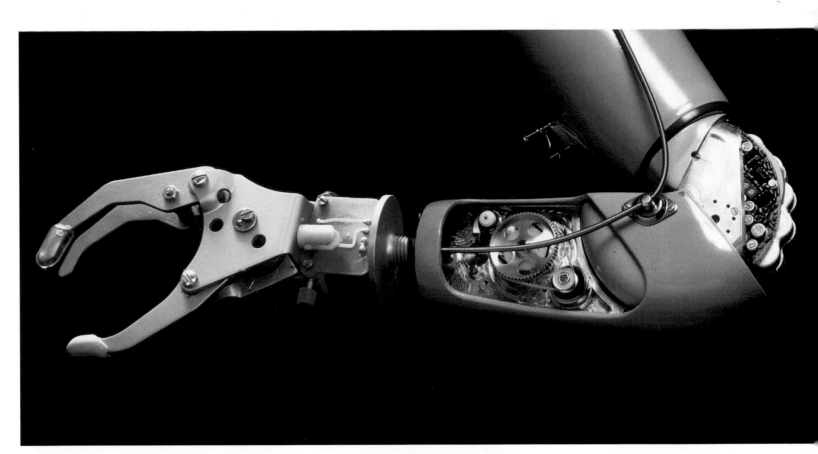

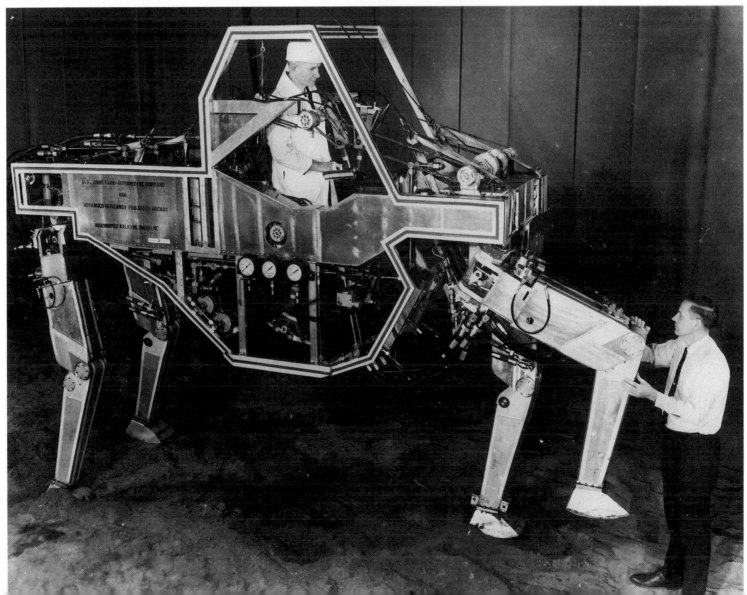

Opposite The fact that most lightweight, human-scale robot arms can handle loads of only a few pounds is no drawback to those whose limbs may be incapable of any movement at all. The freedom from dependence that such an arm could bring to a handicapped person can hardly be exaggerated in its importance for their sense of self-sufficiency and confidence. Similar claims were made for home computers in the 1970s, but, significantly, they proved to be something of a disappointment — mainly because they embody pure decision-making power with no physical muscle.

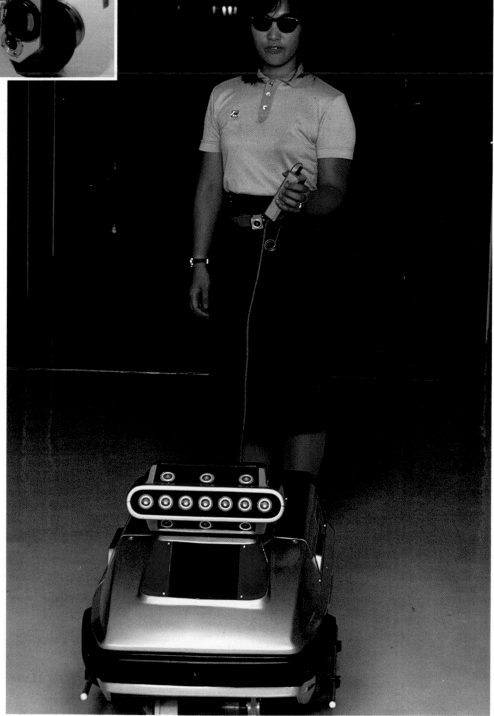

Above and right Robot guide dogs for the blind were first developed in England as aids in training the blind person to trust and respond to a dog. This Japanese robot has a range of sensors, and can carry loads, avoid obstacles and communicate with its owner through the leash — really just a data cable.

Once More With Feeling

The essential nature of the robot, as has been repeatedly stressed, is its programability — the capacity to be taught any action or sequence of actions within its physical powers, and to repeat that sequence exactly and without limit. This and autonomy are central concepts defining the robot ideal.

Machines have long been programable. Music boxes, for example, are probably the oldest examples, containing revolving drums covered in patterns of projections which trip the keys of the box, thus producing the tune represented by the patterns. In most such devices one drum can be replaced by another, thus programing a different tune. A slightly more complex development of this idea is the pianola and the player-piano: tunes are represented by holes punched in a roll of paper led through a reader, which depresses the piano keys to produce the tune. Sophisticated versions can record some of the original player's dynamics — certainly the pedaling, and sometimes the legato and rubato. Indeed, a player piano roll of *Rhapsody In Blue* and *American In Paris* played by the composer, George Gershwin, in 1933 was recently recorded on disk in stereo with a modern orchestral backing.

These techniques appeared in industry in the control of machinery such as lathes and milling machines. The program took the form of a string of numbers representing settings for the various parts of the machine, and were read from punched paper tape or decks of punched cards. Later, magnetic tape became the program medium of these Numerically Controlled (NC) machines.

Robots can be educated by writing a computer program in advance, and then reading it into the robot's control circuitry — again from magnetic disk or tape — and this is a very useful way of teaching robots known and tested application sequences. Developing programs like this may be done by a programer sitting at a console testing the developing program on a real robot, but this can be expensive and impractical; a cheaper and more satisfactory method is computer simulation, in which a three-dimensional perspective model of the robot and its workplace can be drawn by the computer on a VDU screen. The robot program is then applied to the simulated robot so that the programer can observe the program's performance under all conditions. This can be an improvement on on-site program development, especially since it permits ideas about design of the workplace to be tested in conjunction with the simulated performance of the robot.

The most commonly used method of programing robots, however, is teaching by example. A human operator takes the end effector of the arm through the sequence of operations that it is intended to perform and the robot "learns" every step of the way by rote. Large manipulators may be equipped with a scaled-down "teaching arm" which simulates the main arm's characteristics but is more amenable to precise human movement. Alternatively, the robot may be controlled in its "learn" mode through a control pad of keys and joysticks; each joint of the arm in turn is moved until the human operator is satisfied with the arm's attitude and position, when he or she presses a button to signify that the robot should "memorize" the entire position (described by the angles or positions of all the joints in the robot). In either case, the educated robot can be made to repeat its operator's instructions in an edit-playback mode, whereby the operator can halt the sequence at any point to change the programed moves and positions. The controller software provides these facilities, and others, such as optimization: when the human operator is satisfied that the main positions in the sequence have been satisfactorily established by the robot, the controller works out the "optimal" paths between those points, taking into account the robot's characteristics such as speed, joint rotation ranges, geometry and flexibility.

Optimization is appropriate only when the robot is being taught a point-to-point task, such as picking up an item from one bin and placing it in another. How the arm moves between those points is irrelevant to the performance of the task, unless, of course, the optimal path causes a collision with part of the work place; in that case the operator must specify intermediate points between source and destination so that the path is recalculated through safe areas. Not all applications are of the point-to-point kind, however: a common industrial application is paint-spraying and this requires the robot to follow a complex and often irregular three-dimensional trajectory. This must be learned wholesale from the operator, and is called "continuous-path movement."

The above methods are applicable when the task at hand requires no feedback or decision-making; when these features are present in the task, then the robot must be programed by more or less conventional computing methods. This can be done in a variety of ways depending upon the nature of the robot controller, the task to be programed and the programer's preference. Some robots have to be programed as if they were extensions of the controlling computer (instead of its *raison d 'être),* and so might require programs written in any of the conventional computer languages such as BASIC or FORTRAN. Others have their own programing language built in, such as IBM's AML and Unimation's VAL. Because these languages are specialized, they make life much easier for the programer, and should result in more efficient programs, reflected ultimately in the performance of the robot.

Left *Just as the robot dog teaches its owner, so humans teach robots many things — this man instructing the robot in valve insertion could be teaching himself out of a job.*

Right *Picking auto parts out of their storage bins in an efficient non-damaging way is a skill more easily and cheaply taught than learned.*

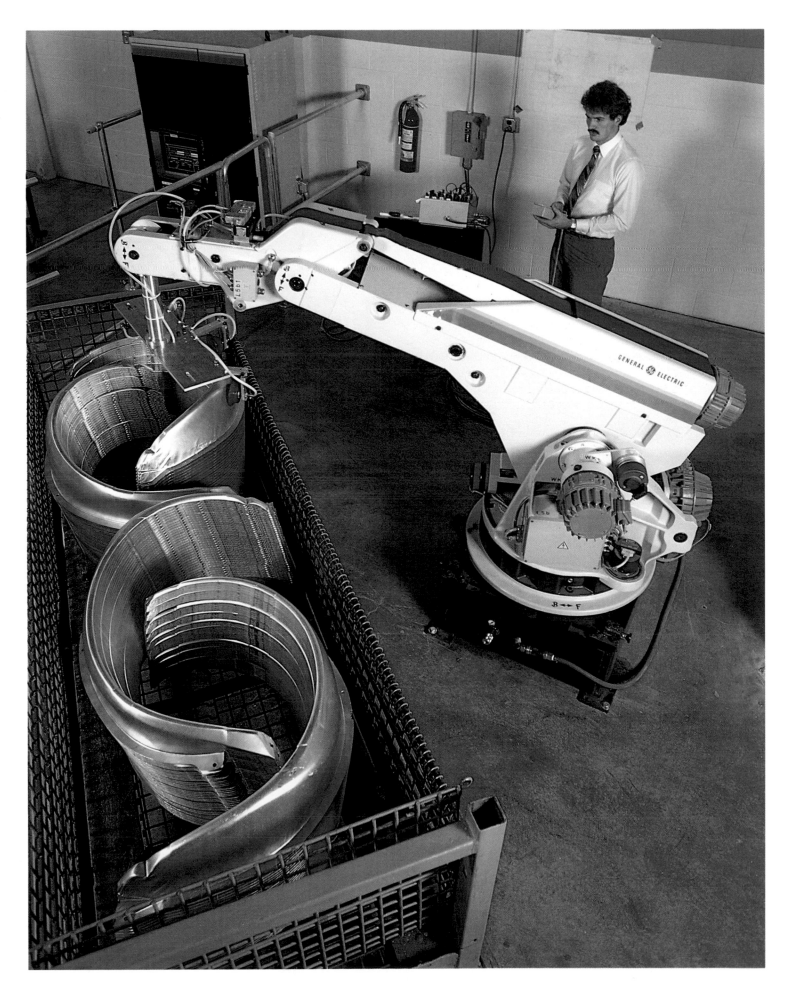

States Of Mind

Many robots require programs which do not prescribe or describe a particular task, but rather enable the robot to apprehend the real world in particular ways, make its own action decisons, and even develop its own strategies based upon what it experiences. This takes us into the deep waters of artificial intelligence (AI) and knowledge processing (usually represented in the acronym, IKBS – Intelligent Knowledge-Based Systems). Programs written in these areas consist of a database containing the known facts about a state or task or place, a rule-set for generating action on the basis of observed or known events, and a strategy processor for changing old rules, developing new ones, and editing the contents of the database as experience demands. AI has been a high-intensity research priority in robotics and computing for many years, but the setbacks have been as many as the successes, and of greater significance. Because of the successes of technological programs such as the space race, and the development of microchip technology, most of us expect that problems need simply be stated to be solved; perhaps a little more money and time need be spent here, and a few more reseachers employed there, but, in general, science delivers the goods; AI doesn't seem to be like that. One member of the prestigious Artificial Intelligence Research Unit of Edinburgh University, Scotland, recently said, "It's taken us fifteen years not quite to get where I expected to be after five months in 1970." The work requires,

typically, large amounts of computing power, which makes its techniques impractical as yet for use in autonomous robots.

As we have seen before, however – with Grey Walter's "tortoises" for example – simple methods can produce apparently complex behavior, and the various maze-solving robots demonstrate this very clearly. Roboticists have used small robot mobiles in desktop mazes for years as testbeds for their theories about intelligence and the control of sensors and movement: Claudee Shannon, the founder of Information Theory, built such a mouse in the 1930s – they're usually called mice, for some reason. A British scientist, Dr. John Billingsley of Portsmouth Polytechnic, England, started a "Micromouse Competition" in the late 1970s for amateur roboticists. The robot mice had to be autonomous, and were designed to explore and then to run a maze, at the center of which was a brass cheese. The mouse that traversed the maze in the shortest time took the brass cheese.

Competitors quickly learned that writing semi-intelligent maze-solving software isn't very difficult (many mazes can be solved simply by following one wall from the entrance until it reaches the exit; the competition invigilators just as quickly discovered how to construct mazes to trap the wall-followers); the chief problems were associated with the mechanical systems of the mouse – stopping and starting and turning accurately, sensing junctions, and steering down the middle of a corridor. Victory in the first years of the competition went to the most reliable and predictable mice,

Right *The purpose of the Micromouse competitions was to stimulate hobbyists' interest in robotic engineering and software techniques. The mice must learn a maze of known dimensions but unknown design within a set "practice" time, then traverse the maze as quickly as possible. The fastest mouse carries away the brass cheese at the center of the maze.*

Below *Started by Dr. John Billingsley of Portsmouth Polytechnic, England, the Micromouse Competitions have lost popularity as mouse-building has become more expert. Billingsley's latest challenge is a robot table-tennis competition.*

not necessarily those with the most advanced software. The straightforward search algorithm is:

1 Enter the maze and go straight ahead
2 At a junction take the leftmost exit, provided that you haven't already taken it or that you didn't arrive at the junction from it
3 When you arrive at a dead end, or at a junction whose every exit is familiar to you, retreat to the previous junction
4 Repeat from Step 2 until the exit is achieved — success — or until you return to the entrance — the maze is blind

This enables a robot to solve any maze, though it needs refinement if a solution is to be found in the fastest possible time, or if the best of all possible paths is required. The problems faced by the micromouse are small-scale versions of those met by a free-ranging autonomous robot in a factory or office, for example. In these settings, the geography of the place can be known or learned very quickly. It is the plethora of unpredictable variations in local geometry that can cause problems for the robot and its programers — suppose somebody moves a table into the corridor, will the robot not "see" it and try to drive underneath it, knocking itself off-balance? Will the robot detect glass doors? Suppose its way is barred temporarily, will it bump in the corridor looking for a way around?

These shortcomings can be allowed for, but limitations on the size of computer and power supply that a mobile robot can carry impose a limit on the amount of data that can be accumulated and processed. Some AI researchers, however, think that these and other software limitations can be solved by adopting a completely different approach to dealing with the environment. They say that the problems are artefacts of the sequential processing structure at the heart of our computers and our thinking about problem-solving. Instead of trying to mimic the human brain on a conventional computer (which, they say, actually behaves nothing like the human brain), we should mimic the construction of the brain

Right *Competitors in the 1984 Euromouse competition, held in Copenhagen, Denmark, display their range of sensors, designs and methods. The ones with the slightly more intelligent expressions are the humans, mostly. Speedy Gonzales is a long-time winner in the British competitions, and another British entry, Thumper, follows the maze walls by looking down either side of them.*

— as far as possible — and study the behavior of the device.

The outcome of this thinking is the neural net system, so called from the neuron, the active agent of the brain cell. Each neuron has several inputs and one output, which may carry messages to the body's muscles via the nervous system, or provide input to other neurons. Nowhere in this system — which at first glance seems to be simply a biological analog of an electronic computer's memory — is there anything resembling a central processor through which the input/output of these cells is invariably routed; nowhere does there seem to be any central controller corresponding to a machine's operating system. Researchers have come to describe intelligence and knowledge as "emergent properties" of the network itself; it has long been a pseudo-fact of science and sci-fi that the number of neurons in a brain determines its processing power, and that some critical neural number or ratio exists such that intelligence inevitably follows in brains exceeding that quantity. Some researchers have, therefore, constructed networks of RAM chips (Random Access Memory, the integrated circuits comprising millions of transistors each capable of representing one binary digit) as analogs of the brain, aided in their researches by the steadily falling cost of memory devices. Work began in England in the mid-1960s, and in 1972 a team at the University of Kent, England, produced the MINERVA system, which achieved remarkable success in recognizing hand-written characters, given definitions of their idealized, printed shapes, and did it with response times far faster than conventional computer methods could achieve. Some of this team moved to Brunel University, England, and produced in 1981 the WISARD system (for Wilkie, Aleksander and Stonham's Recognition Device) which scored 100 per cent in tests involving recognition of fifteen human faces — live faces, with all the variability of image produced by light and shade, mood and expression. The system is now available commercially as a pattern-recognition device for robots and other devices, but the implications of this line of research for artificial and robot intelligence cannot be overemphasized.

Robots at Home

"Put down that wrench!"
Blowups Happen — *Robert Heinlein*

We have seen how the general image of a robot breaks down on inspection to mobiles, manipulators and others, so that we start to recognize as robotic anything that possesses some of the crucial robotic characteristics. The domestic robot is a figure of modern myth — no golem, certainly, but not ET, either; perhaps somewhere between C3P0 and Woody Allen's whacky robotic waiter in *Sleeper*. You can buy that sort of robot, and some people may get some use out of them. More particular classes of robots, however, can be discerned in the home, such as toys, educational arms, construction sets, mobiles, and so on. Whether robots will make a significant showing in the home as servants or service agents remains to be seen: the computer has made no particular impact on the organization and maintenance of the home, though the microchip is to be found in much domestic equipment. More likely, new robotic techniques will increasingly influence the design of domestic appliances without necessarily changing their appearance or central function — washing machines, stoves, vacuum cleaners, food processors, entertainment centers might all benefit from touch sensing, or intelligent manipulators, or vision systems. The trouble with this kind of measured, sensible projection is that it's usually shown to be asinine or inane within a few years of its utterance — Mr. Watson, who steered IBM to power through its formative years, one of the giants of the industry, sagely predicted that there would be a world market for a total of five computers.

Domestic Robots

These machines are not cheap. They range from $1,000 to $5,000, and may bring you status or entertainment but little else of practical value. They are battery-powered mobiles standing about 3ft in height, and weighing up to 100lbs. The manufacturers variously describe them as "free-roving," "self-contained" and "educational"; none of which actually means "useful," you notice.

The RB5X is a domed cylindrical object with a single five-axis arm. It travels on three wheels and is ringed about its base with collision detectors; these supplement its range-finding equipment, which is based on the ultrasonic system developed for automatic focusing in cameras.

TOPO, from Androbot, is an appealing manikin from the man who founded Atari Computers, Nolan Bushnell. It has only two wheels, splayed outwards at alarming angles, which apparently give it stability and controllability. It communicates with an Apple II personal computer via an infra-red link, and it does have a stored repertoire of synthesized speech. Since it possesses no arm or other manipulator (though it does have a fold-down shelf, shown in the publicity photos as comfortably able to hold a small apple), its utility is limited: it can hold the door if somebody opens it, and it's a marvelously expensive moving paperweight. It might frighten a burglar if it fell on him or her.

"A mobile home entertainment system" is how most critics dismiss the Hubot, which consists of a TV, a video games machine, a radio-cassette-recorder, a battery, a motor and some wheels. If it had buttons and a record player, it could be a juke box.

The Hero I from Heath Zenith of Bristol, England, is a little more like the real thing. It has a five-axis arm with gripper, ultrasonic ranging, movement and light-intensity sensors, sound detection and speech synthesis. A keyboard and display screen give access to its computer, while its control circuitry has been made up on removal boards intended for experimentation and development by the owners. It was designed with this in mind, and is intended to stimulate interest in and knowledge of robotics. That may be thought of as useful, certainly.

Opposite *The robot dream, or a trash-can nightmare? If general-purpose domestic robots ever become commonplace, they will have usable arms, a range of end effectors, speech recognition and synthesis and sophisticated vision processing as standard. Whether anyone would employ all that intelligence and capital equipment to boil water and answer the telephone is the pertinent question.*

Right *Entertainment is about all you get from the Androbot TOPO, seen here in its tedious dozens. Lacking any manipulator, it trails expensively around on its two electrically driven wheels, using up valuable computer time with its infra-red link, and frightening the turtles.*

Below *If all robots were like Woody Allen's spoof android servants in* Sleeper, *then most people would want one, simply for the entertainment value.*

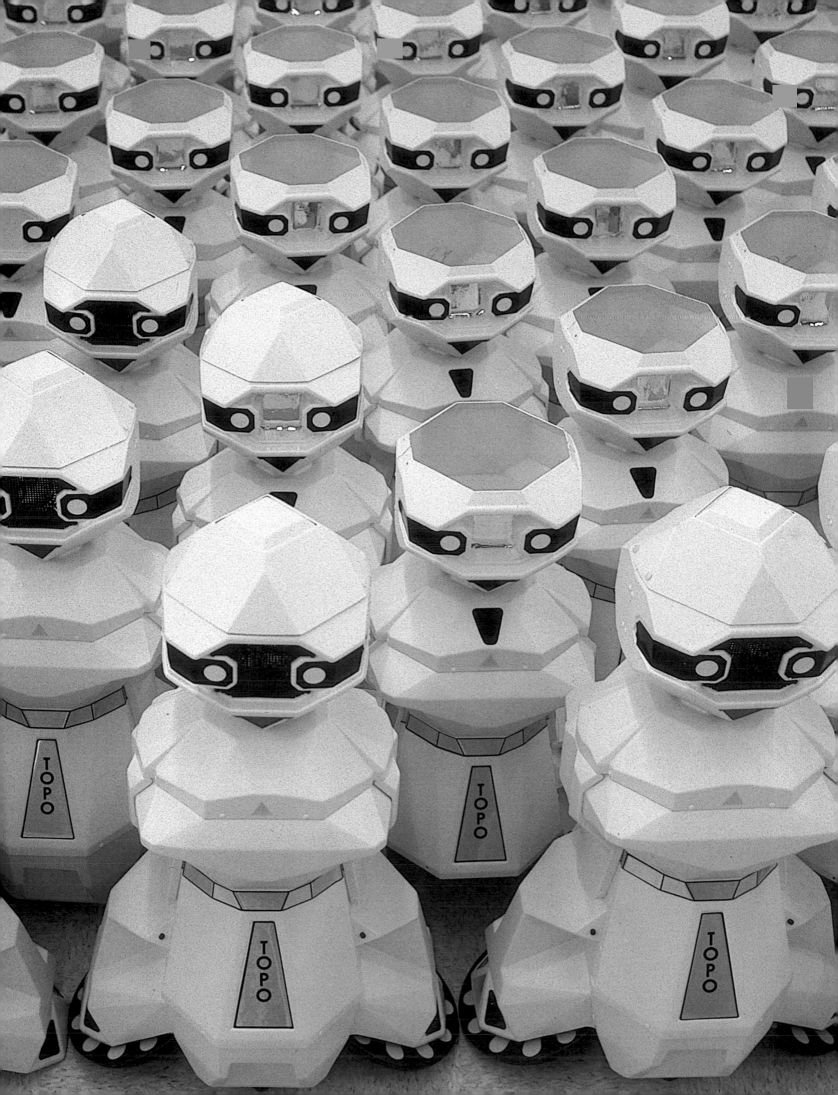

Educational Robot Arms

This has been the major growth area in domestic robots, as it has in industry, and for the same reasons. You still can't really do anything with such an arm that you couldn't do for yourself, except, of course, think about robotics. Which is why they're called educational. They range in price from a few hundred dollars to several thousand, and in propulsion employ all the methods used in industrial manipulators, and more besides: stepper motors are common, and so are conventional hydraulics. The Neptune and Genesis arms, however, both from English manufacturers, employ tap water as their hydraulic medium and pump-assisted mains pressure as their motive power.

Often these arms can be bought in kit form — very much in the educational spirit — and almost all need to be controlled by a personal computer, though nothing very expensive is necessary: the Sinclair-Timex or Commodore Vic-20, for example, costing around $150, will do nicely. These arms can do in small scale most things that their grown-up precursors can, but the scale is small indeed: a typical maximum effective radius of 2ft, and a workload limit of just a quarter-pound. Most have some kind of positional reporting sensors, and often a touch sensor to report whether the gripper is closed. Very few allow a variety of end effectors to be employed; the outstanding exception being the elegant Rhino XR, which, with its open-frame, girder-system construction, chain drive and toothed gears all exposed, looks like something that won a medal at the Philadelphia Home Engineering Exhibition of 1895.

Right *Extra Fischertechnik components have been used in adding a grabber arm (opened and closed by the linear actuator above it) to this assembled BBC Buggy. Though its range of sensors — infra-red line-following, light-sensitive and ultrasonic rangefinding — enables it to navigate reasonably accurately, wheelspin and instability in rough ground like that shown here would quickly upset its calculations.*

Below *As computers gained popularity in homes, schools and summer camps through the 1980s, so children became interested in robotics, usually through using a floor turtle (the perspex domes on the televisions) under the control of LOGO, the educational programing language. The turtle is a floor buggy with accurate stepper motors, a computer link and a pen for tracing out its owner's directions on the floor. LOGO and the turtle turn geometry and computer programing into simple systems for describing the world.*

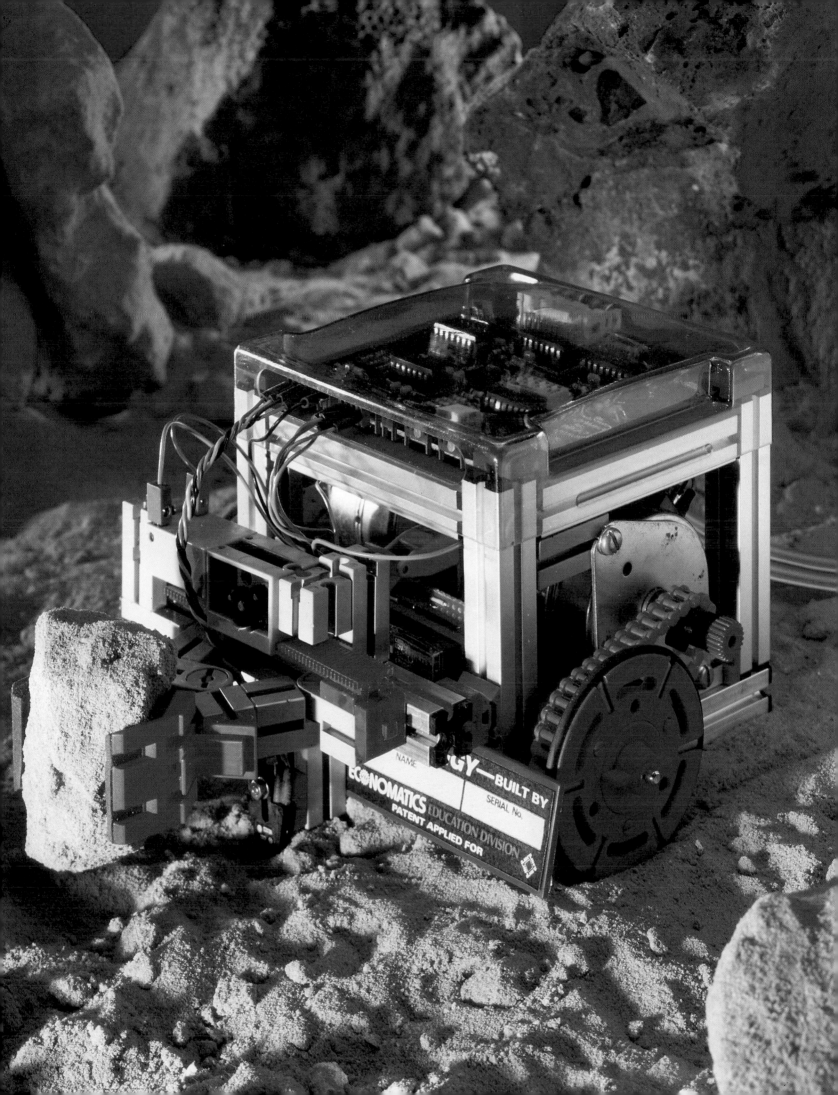

Right *The increasing cheapness of the microchip was given dramatic expression at the end of the 1970s in the work of computer entrepreneurs such as Britain's Clive Sinclair and the US's Steve Wozniak and Chuck Peddle. Sinclair's achievement was to pack whole computer systems into small well designed boxes at bargain prices, so that the computer, no matter how unfriendly and primitive it might even then have seemed, became as commonplace a part of home and work as the watch or ball-point pen.*

Left *The BBC Buggy is an inexpensive robot construction kit for use with the popular BBC home computer. The structural components are from Fischertechnik. It is equipped with light sensors and collision detectors as standard. Many owners have cannibalized it for other robotic projects.*

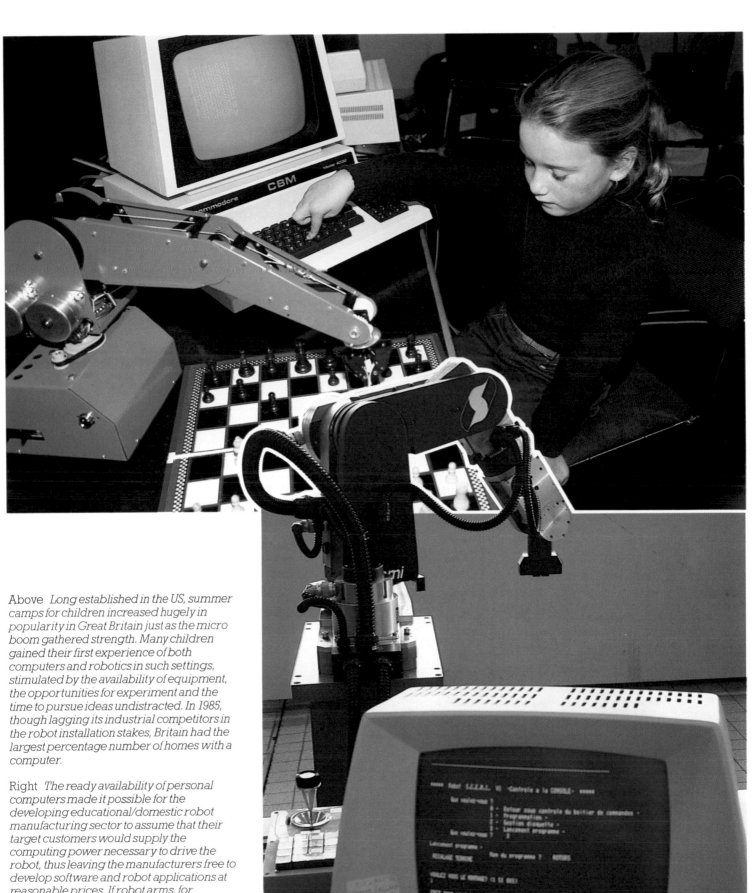

Above *Long established in the US, summer camps for children increased hugely in popularity in Great Britain just as the micro boom gathered strength. Many children gained their first experience of both computers and robotics in such settings, stimulated by the availability of equipment, the opportunities for experiment and the time to pursue ideas undistracted. In 1985, though lagging its industrial competitors in the robot installation stakes, Britain had the largest percentage number of homes with a computer.*

Right *The ready availability of personal computers made it possible for the developing educational/domestic robot manufacturing sector to assume that their target customers would supply the computing power necessary to drive the robot, thus leaving the manufacturers free to develop software and robot applications at reasonable prices. If robot arms, for example, costing $200 had to be sold with a computer, then the price would rise to something like $450 — a significant difference in any market, but especially so when new products of unproven worth appear and disappear so regularly.*

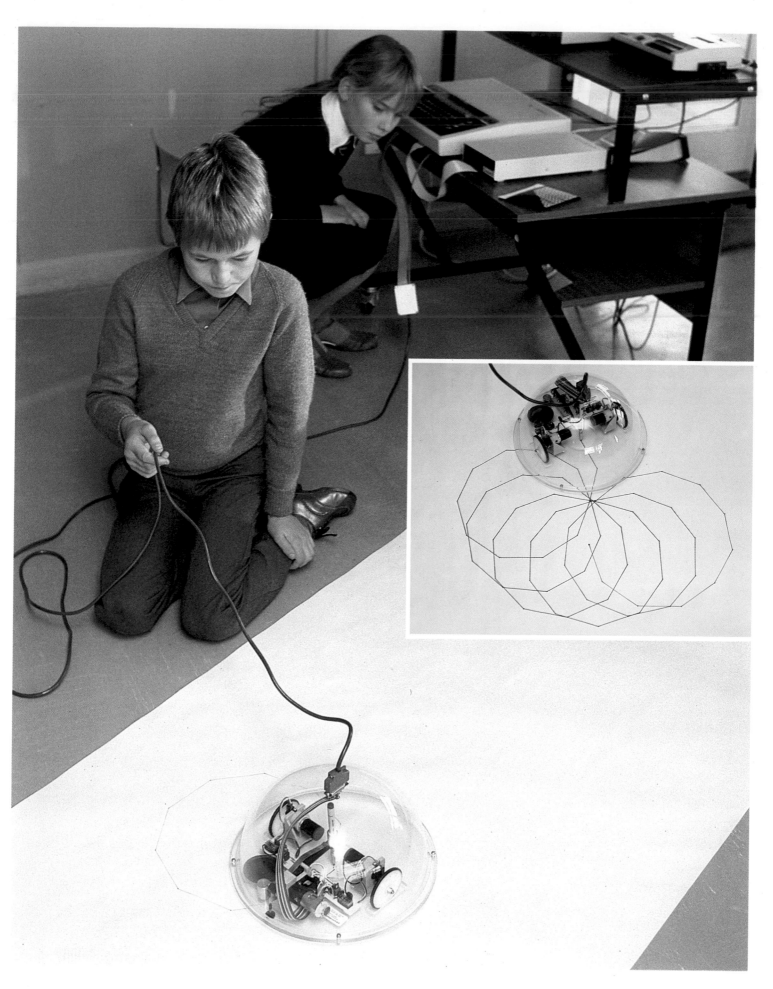

Left *In his book,* Mindstorms, *teacher and mathematician Seymour Papert described how a set of gear wheels fascinated him as a child, becoming an imaginative "micro-world" in which his play and fantasy spilled naturally over into explorations of physics, math and dynamics.*

Left inset *Using stepper motors and on-board control circuitry, even quite cheap floor turtles — costing less than $100, say — can achieve remarkable positional accuracy; tolerances of $\frac{1}{16}$ in tracing a circle of 1 yard diameter are common.*

Right *The figures that the turtle traces on the floor can be simulated by LOGO as a graphics turtle on the computer screen — more convenient than real objects, but much less Papertian in spirit.*

Below *Computers are OK in this world view, but they can only mirror your own thoughts, achievements and failings; dirtying your hands in the intractable world of real objects, where mass, inertia and friction aren't just numbers is an essential of Papert's view of education.*

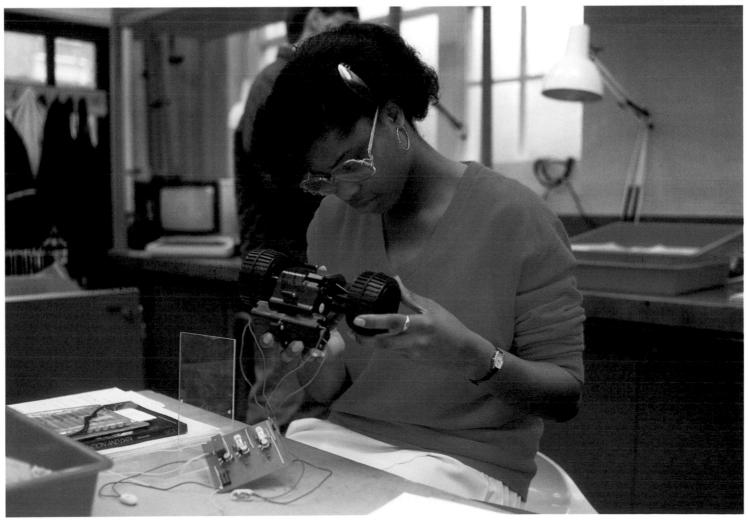

Robot Toys

These range from models of cars that somehow fold and twist to become space monsters to a robot revision aid, and are generally amusing and sometimes instructive. Mechanical toys have a long history, stretching back through the toymakers of Germany in the Middle Ages to Hero and his water-powered tableaux in 300 BC. The model robot as toy first appears in the 1940s and 1950s, the great days of Erector Sets (Meccano), and the sci-fi film, and the comic book. The real thing, however, had to wait for the computer. In 1972 Leachim, a 200lbs, 6ft horror built by Michael Freeman, became one of the first teaching robots. It had flashing lights, subject information recorded on audio cassettes, and a telephone dial through which children dialled the answers to questions put by Leachim. In 1978 a 1ft high descendant of Leachim called 2-XL was mass-produced and sold in toy shops. It's a stubby little plastic model with a primitive keyboard through which answers to its audio-cassette-generated questions can be entered; in addition to the questions, the tapes contain the answers and further information on the topic. A range of subjects is covered by different cassettes.

Milton Bradley's Big Trak is a six-wheeled toy truck driven by electric motors, which rolls around in response to movement commands keyed in through a numeric keypad on its "flatbed." These commands can be linked together in sequences — computer programs, in fact. Many robot enthusiasts have bought this toy and connected it to a home computer, thus achieving far more programing power.

Using Big Trak or other similar toys as computer-driven robots can be a cheap alternative to buying educational floor robots built for the task. These are computer-controlled "buggies" intended to instruct in robotic techniques; they are programable, have open access electronics, feature a range of sensors and the capability to add more, and can usually carry a pen, thus becoming "turtles."

Harking back, perhaps unconsciously, to Grey Walter's "electric tortoises," the turtle moves around the floor, usually tracing out its path in pen for later study. It is controlled by cable or infra-red link to a personal computer, probably running the educational language called LOGO. This is the result of the educational views of Seymour Papert, a US educationist, who wants to use computers and robots (and everything else, of course) to allow children to create "microworlds" in which through play they teach themselves about physics and math and English and about education itself. The floor turtle (which can be simulated on the screen as well) is controlled by commands such as FORWARD and RIGHT, which require the child to think in geometric terms, though quite naturally. The structure of the language makes the development of complicated programs a step-by-step process, and the operating principle is to make success as achievable as possible, so error messages are helpful and non-punitive. LOGO is appearing on computers in many classrooms, and may turn out to be the most significant single factor in increasing children's awareness of robots.

Below *Milton Bradley's Big Trak is a programable truck, combining the ruggedness of the BBC Buggy with the educational appeal of a floor turtle. It can be interfaced to a home computer by anyone prepared to tinker with its circuitry, thus providing a sturdy, reasonably accurate floor turtle at a low price.*

Right *These attractive toys come in part-assembled kit form, and will run around in simple maneuvres responding to a high-pitched whistle or a clap of the hands.*

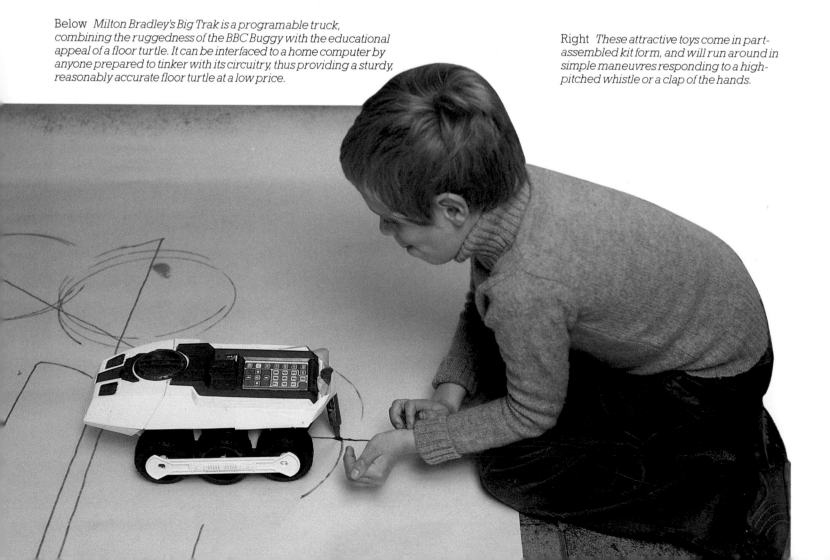

Previous pages *The number and range of mobile and static robot toys is some indication of increasing public and commercial interest in the subject.*

Left *The Tomy Verbot is similar in principle to Big Trak in that movement is controlled through its on-board key-pad; it can be trained, however, to perform sequences of movements in response to commands spoken into the voice controller.*

Right *These ceramic robots by Ditto Reproductions don't actually do anything but they do look pretty.*

Below *Like Big Trak, the Tomy Robo 1 is a fascinating toy with strong links to the "real" world of work. Controlled by the joysticks and the energy level panel, it can be made to pick and place objects with reasonable precision.*

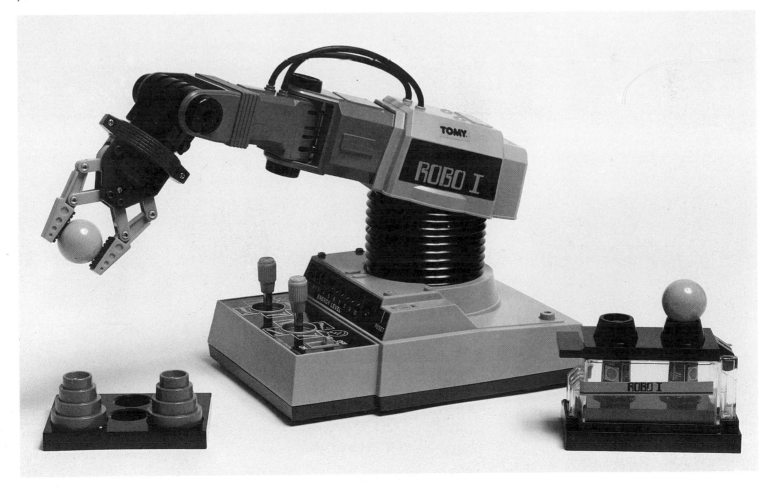

Other Ideas

Robots and robotic influences are penetrating the home through dance and the TV, while they frequently also appear in shop windows and discotheques. Children in New York streets in the early 1980s began moving and dancing to pop music in an eerie robotic fashion, probably in response to the kind of robot-arm footage that was starting to appear in automobile advertisements and newscasts about Japanese industrial might. The fad became a "dance craze," spreading to Europe and the Far East within a couple of years. Robot mannequins appeared in shop windows modelling clothes around this time, though mechanical versions had been in use long before this; the Original Android Company of London, England, supplies programable mannequins with a high degree of flexibility for just this purpose. Cheaper versions of these robots began to appear as novelties in discotheques around 1983, though performance artists such as "Professor" Bruce Lacey had been experimenting with robot dancers since the early 1970s. Sony, the Japanese electronics firm, produced a memorable series of TV advertisements in 1983 featuring talking robotic household appliances: the bland affability of the faithful robot servant/mentor projected by R2D2 of *Star Wars* has been eclipsed by the waspish mania of John Cleese's robot vacuum cleaner.

Some other recent robotic news items point to future domestic robot possibilities:

1   A robot patient is available to medical students in some schools; it has sight, sound and touch sensors, a temperature, pulse, heartbeat and breathing. It can be made to exhibit various conditions, such as cardiac arrest, and to respond appropriately to treatment.

2   Dental students in Atlanta, Georgia, are using robot heads for surgical practice; they have opening mouths, pink tongues, and white teeth, which exhibit a range of disorders and decay. Sensors in the teeth enable the head to simulate pain, speech synthesis produces squawks and cries of "Ouch, dat hurd." In the next versions they'll bleed and simulate convulsions and strangulation.

3   A robot guide dog has been developed by the Mechanical Engineering Laboratory of Great Britain's Ministry of Industry. Called the Meldog Mk I, it is the size of a spaniel, powered by rechargeable batteries. It runs on wheels 3ft ahead of its user, and vibrates the leash if it steps out of a pre-defined safety zone. It is intended initially to train users in the use of guide dogs before they get their own animals; future versions will communicate more with the user, will have light and sound sensors enabling them to move more intelligently, and may be programed to disobey commands that may take its user into danger.

4   The Nippon Telegraph and Telephone Company have developed a robot with hands that can turn the pages of almost any book, given the chance to gauge the thickness and "feel" of the book first.

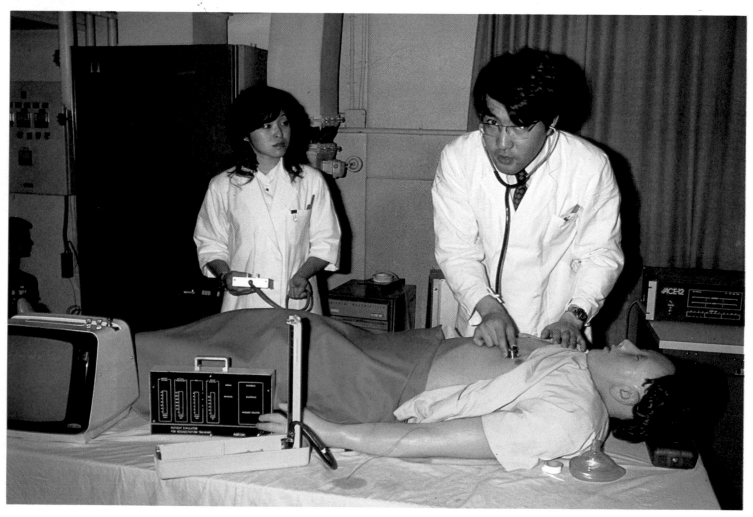

Above and right *Reasonably cheap Sat-Nav systems have long been available for yachtsmen and fisherfolk; many auto manufacturers are talking about installing radio links in their cars, backed up by a laser-disk library of maps and communications protocols. It is a cliché of fact and fiction that the sleeper on waking asks "Where am I?" Now your car will know better than you, so which is better informed, and which is in charge? Cars will undoubtedly follow this route to system domination in their robotic control equipment — in the very real cause of safety.*

Left *Androids do come in useful: this medical practice aid maintains a pulse, heartbeat and respiration rate, and simulates various pathologies or trauma such as cardiac arrest. It then responds — or not — to students' attempts to revive and resuscitate it. Such practice is unavailable to students except by these means.*

Robots in Space

"I lingered round them, under that benign sky: watched the moths fluttering among the heather and hare-bells; listened to the soft wind breathing through the grass; and wondered how anyone could ever imagine unquiet slumbers for the sleepers in that unquiet earth." Wuthering Heights — *Emily Brontë*

Space robotics on TV — live! If ever the Robot Age could be said to have dawned, it was in April 1985 when viewers around the world watched the crew of the US Space Shuttle constructing a new end effector for their craft's 48ft long Remote Manipulator System. They were attempting to dock with an errant satellite, and needed to trip a switch on its side before they could safely approach it. The team used what materials they could find — wire and plastic torn from a drinks carton — under the coaching of scientists in laboratories on Earth who could try out their solutions on lab simulations. This absorbing interlude had all the familiar ingredients of real life technical endeavor: an unexpected problem in inconvenient circumstances, makeshift materials, untried solutions, and a bunch of on-line smart alecks telling you what to do from the comfort of their back seats. True to form, the first attempt at interplanetary home robotics was a failure — but an educational failure; future missions will carry emergency kits of paper-clips, matchsticks, old light bulbs and copies of *The Whole Earth Catalog* to facilitate emergency repairs. Shipboard entertainment systems will include video cassettes of Sam Shepard and Michael Jackson in Antonioni's *Zen and the Art of Motorcycle Maintenance.*

Space was made for robots, and robots for space. Earth has no environment as remote and hostile, so difficult to attain, so expensive to inhabit. Humans may never go further into space than the Moon, but their robots will certainly explore the Solar System, perhaps colonize some of it. H.G. Wells' sci-fi novel, *The War Of The Worlds,* written in 1898, depicted the invasion of Earth by Martian creatures using death rays and three-legged exoskeleton land craft. A disturbing precognition of The Robots' Return, perhaps?

So far, space missions have used remote manipulation of robotic devices. In the first US Moon missions, the Surveyor dug a trench and analyzed surface samples under radio guidance from Earth, took photographs of possible landing sites, and used radioactive sensors to investigate the lunar soil. At the same time, the USSR Lunar Sample Return Missions took samples from the Moon's surface and deposited them in the return capsule, which took off from the Moon and returned to Earth.

The USSR's Lunokhod 1 was the first wheeled vehicle on the Moon. It landed in November 1970 and over the next ten months roamed the Moon's surface. It was powered by solar cells and batteries, the latter warmed in the interior of the craft by a radioactive isotope heater. As it explored the Moon, or a few square miles of it, under the control of a four-person team on Earth, it transmitted 20,000 photographs and gigabytes of data from its various sensors. These included seismological sensors, autonomous obstacle detection and avoidance software, and stereoscopic TV cameras. It was tracked on the surface by Crimean and French observatories bouncing laser beams off its laser mirror.

The US Mars probe in 1976 landed the Viking 1 on the surface of Mars, and was controlled from Earth despite the 38 minute distance-imposed delay between action on Mars and direction from Earth. The Viking carried a six-axis arm, was static on its tripod legs, and contained two chemical laboratories, a weather station, a seismology station, photographic processing equipment, and two computers.

The Viking's arm was the first in Space, but the US Space Shuttle's Remote Manipulator System is the best to date. It is the biggest robot arm ever built, and cost $24 million to develop. It has so far been used to launch satellites, lifting them from the craft's hold, and positioning them accurately. In free-fall it can safely manipulate loads of up to 15 tons mass. The shipboard operator uses two controlling joysticks and feedback from TV cameras at the elbow and the wrist.

Future planetary exploration will feature increasing robotic autonomy — the static Viking 1 was not terribly restricted by the delay in Earth-Mars communication, but a mobile would have to have independent intelligent sensing systems and decision-making onboard computers. Orbital devices such as the space telescopes will need robotic equipment for control of the craft's attitude and instruments. The equipment developed will no doubt spring from the laboratories that design the proposed US "Star Wars" Strategic Defense Initiative. The number and variety of

Looking like a large light bulb, this craft descended into the Venusian atmosphere in 1978.

transmission and monitoring satellites grows apace; there may be a future for some kind of orbital maintenance robot, perhaps launched from, and retrievable by, a shuttle. It should be able to locate and dock with other craft, and armed with a good manipulator should be able to perform quite extensive repairs and maintenance under remote control. Such an arm might well be a hybrid remote/autonomous manipulator, in that its software could contain a repertoire of modular actions activated by a single command, such as "Unscrew This Nut" or "Replace This Chip," thus augmenting the remote controller's directions.

Such an orbiting robot is feasible now, and almost economical, given the costs of having a multi-million dollar satellite rendered useless by a simple mechanical fault. It should lead naturally on to the space hard-hat, the interplanetary construction worker, building and then operating space antennae, power stations and construction platforms. These structures are possible now, given the kind of funding that the Moon programs of the 1960s and 1970s attracted, and would probably have far more immediate pay-off; it is doubtful, though, what political will or economic justification exists for such an effort. The US Space Shuttle missions started conducting experiments in material science in 1983, and there is much commercial interest in the possibility of new high-value processes in space such as convection-free cooling of melted solids, processing of molten samples without containers, alloying through in *vacuo* zero-gravity diffusion and electrophoretic separation of biological surfaces. These might form the basis of a space materials-processing industry run by robot equipment, while robot craft "mine" the asteroid belt, prospecting for lumps of nickel, tin, and iridium as big as Coney Island. On the Moon and other planets, robot machines could perform the same processing functions, and extract minerals and chemicals from the Moon's soil for dispatch to Earth, or for use in the processing plants. Or for the secret construction of a strain of robot *wunderkind,* armed to the teeth, thirsting for revenge, in league with every stoat in the Wild Wood, and plotting, plotting, plotting...*Die Krotetag!*

If any of this marvelous future is to take place, the robot is the one sure feature. Space is an expensive place to maintain humans, but almost benign for robots. Certainly no more hostile than the depths of the sea, nor as servile as the Jockey Shorts production line.

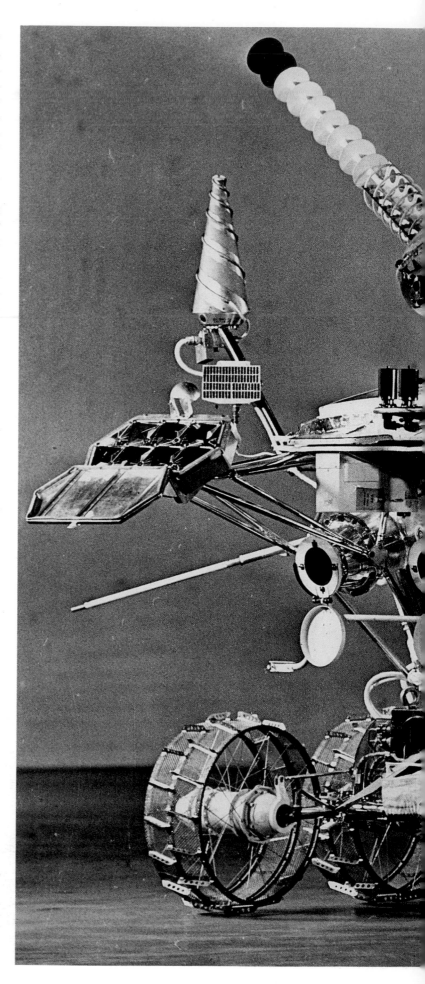

Right *The marvelous exploits of the USSR's Lunokhod are a fully-formed space epic. The first wheeled craft (from Earth) on the Moon, it surveyed and explored for ten months in 1970, collecting and transmitting data under the remote control of its Earth-bound crew of four. The range of its probes and sensors, its array of solar power cells, and its graceful independently sprung wheels mark out Lunokhod as a serious step in the direction of the robot exploration of space.*

Left *A Jet Pak-toting crew member of the US Space Shuttle floats in Earth orbit next to the interplanetary robot arm! Suddenly, all the dreams and stories of the post-war generations are coming true, usually on live television — but only about half as fast as the socio-political myths of that time crumble before our jaded eyes.*

Below *Fifty feet in length, powered by six servomotors and designed for launching and capturing satellites, the Space Shuttle's Remote Manipulator System is an impressive sight even in a Toronto workshop. All the Earth spacecraft that have landed off-Earth, have been equipped with arms, some remote controlled, others far more independent; space is a serious place, and robot arms are significant tools.*

Opposite *Space is a hostile environment, but Venus and some of the other planets are bad neighborhoods. Craft like this "Venus-15" high-orbit atmospheric survey station, from the USSR, built to explore these extremes of pressure and temperature, must be strong and sturdy, and crewed by robots.*

Right *Sensors aloft, crawler tracks working their way across the unpredictable surface of Mars, the future successor of NASA's Viking probe as foreseen by a TV special effects crew: the joint US-European Mars Rover.*

Below *Without the Ion-Drive, or Hyper-Warp Translation, we are barred from deep space by the time taken to travel the enormous distances. Robots will make these journeys into the unknown for us; once they were our dreams, now they steal them for themselves.*

Above *If industrial depletion of Earth's resources continues at the pace of the last century, then planetary and interplanetary mining and chemical processing industries may become economically feasible, given a ready pool of indefatigable robot laborers, roughnecks and roustabouts. The cost and productivity of robot labor will be a crucial factor in the finances of these sci-fi industries.*

Left *A few hundred humans may commute between Earth and Moon to establish and supervize the robot colonies and factories. Food can be grown hydroponically — without soil — on the moon, but air and water must be found. Robots could tunnel for ice in the Moon's crust, and crush the surface rocks to release chemically trapped oxygen for the human colonies. The robots could wreck the environment on our behalf, in fact, before we ever get there.*

Robots in Fiction

"I Sing The Body Electric"
Ray Bradbury

We owe the word "robot" to a playwright, we have a whole ethical and ethological robot bestiary in the works of a science-fiction writer, and our clearest visual images of the robot come from two films, one from the 1920s, and one from the 1970s. The makers of fiction and fantasy have been as important to the Robot Age as roboticists ten times their number. In their prescient imaginings or their artistic disregard for mundane facts, they may have "created facts," may have invented robots and robotic concepts that bear no trace of robot reality, yet most of them have lived to see their dreams turned into fact. The agents of this metamorphosis have not, of course, been the uncaring tides of history and scientific method — they have been the women and men who as children and adults over the last century read H.G. Wells and Edgar Rice Burroughs and Isaac Asimov and Arthur C. Clarke (the greatest and the second greatest living sci-fi writers, though not necessarily in that order), who watched *Metropolis* and *Frankenstein* and *Robot Monster* and *The Wizard of Oz* and *Der Golem,* who then went out and worked for Unimation and IBM and the Space Program and MIT and all the other robot nurseries. Few of us have the chance to give physical expression to our dreams, fewer still see them on TV flying around in space or walking the Moon. The people who managed to convince hard-headed fellow-scientists, politicians and administrators that the Lunokhod should be bombarded with laser rays from Earth, that the astronauts should have the Jet Pak, that the Space Shuttle should be called "Enterprise," and that the extra-solar system space missions should carry a gold tablet of welcome and friendship for the eyes and ears of extraterrestrial salvage merchants, must have greeted every new day of their working lives with the chorus from some space cadet anthem and exhorted themselves in the bathroom mirror to "Win This One For Buck Rogers!" *Si Monumentum requiris, circumspice.*

Sci-Fi Robots

H.G. Wells' *War Of The Worlds* (1898) may be an unwitting precognition of exoskeletons and laser weapons, but the first robots as such do not enter the fictional stage until 1921, when Karel Capek's play *R.U.R (Rossum's Universal Robots)* was performed in Prague, followed by a 1922 performance in New York. On a mysterious island, a satisfactorily "bananas" scientist produces slave androids from bio-engineering techniques, plastics technology and hi-tech metals. His island is staffed by these slaves, who labor in the factory to turn out a comprehensive range of high-quality robots for export. As the robot population grows around the world, rebellion begins amidst their ranks, culminating in insurrection and an attack upon the island itself. The cause, it seems, is left-wing adventurists on the Home Team, screwing up a sound business — the Head of the Physiological Department has been giving the robots souls! And, as the Epilogue makes clear, gender. The robots walk into the final curtain, set on creating their own version of the Robot Age. If the visions of mercenary armies of robot drones struggling on hideous battlefields at the whim of their uncaring masters, then turning against them in the name of robot "humanity" and The Soul can be seen to have roots in the world war just preceding the play's appearance, the major influences in Capek's story are actually the classic myths and images of history, and their fascination with the mystery of life and the consequences of distorting nature's way.

In 1926 the first "pulp magazine" devoted to science fiction appeared in the US: Hugo Gernsback's *Amazing Stories* founded a line of popular science fiction vehicles which has been probably the most significant single influence on the imaginations of three generations of scientists. From their lurid covers, designers, artists, film makers, and technicians took their ideas of how "The Future" ought to look, from their contents the plots of films and novels were mined, pilfered and plagiarized. The fins on the Cadillac and the "Star Wars" Strategic Defense Initiative are both the direct expressions of "Amazing's" *Weltanschauung.*

Right *The mythic journey of Dorothy and her friends to the Land of Oz showed the softer side of the robot image for once, as the gentle Tin Man mooned and dawdled along the Yellow Brick Road in his quest for a heart, that he might love and be loved.*

Left *Modestly described — by himself — as the world's greatest living sci-fi author, Isaac Asimov coined the world "robotics" in the early 1940s, and brought new life to jurisprudence with his stories of robot-human encounters under the immortal Three Laws Of Robotics.*

Bottom *The chief wordsmith, of course, no matter how slim his portfolio, is Karel Capek (opposite top left) who first used the Czech world "robota" (meaning forced labor) in the modern sense in his 1917 story* Opilec. *These scenes (here and opposite top right and bottom) are from his better-known play about robot slaves on a mad scientists' island fortress,* R.U.R. (Rossum's Universal Robots): *"Some renegade has been giving the robots souls — and gender!"*

In 1939 *Amazing Stories* included the first published work of Isaac Asimov, a young chemistry student. That year he graduated and visited the New York World Fair where he saw "Elektro," a mechanical robot made by the Westinghouse Electric Company, respond to spoken commands. In 1958 he became a full-time writer, the inventor of robotics, the robot's Freud, Moses and Psalmist.

Asimov's first robot story was *Robbie,* originally published in 1940 as *Strange Bedfellow.* Its robot is a domestic servant and friend who is infected by human emotions, becoming economically useless. In *Evidence* (1946) the plot turns on a politician's true nature — human or android? In *Satisfaction Guaranteed* (1951) Claire, an alienated woman in a middle-class suburban prison of a home, falls in love with her domestic robot, a plastic-skin test-marketing job called Tony from US Robots. Her chief motive, it seems, is intoxication with the fact that Tony seems to be attracted to her; Tony, however, acting in what he, Svengali-like, conceives to be his client's best interests, has engineered this relationship for the sake of her self-image. This is an early statement of what was to be Asimov's greatest contribution to the entire field of science — fiction and fact — the Three Laws of Robotics. These were developed by Asimov and the SF fanzine editor John W. Campbell in 1940, and their exposition and Talmudic exegesis have been Asimov's chief artistic endeavour. They are:

1 A robot may not injure a human being, or, through inaction, allow a human being to come to harm.

2 A robot must obey the orders given it by human beings except where such orders would conflict with the First Law.

3 A robot must protect its own existence as long as such protection does not conflict with the First or Second Law.

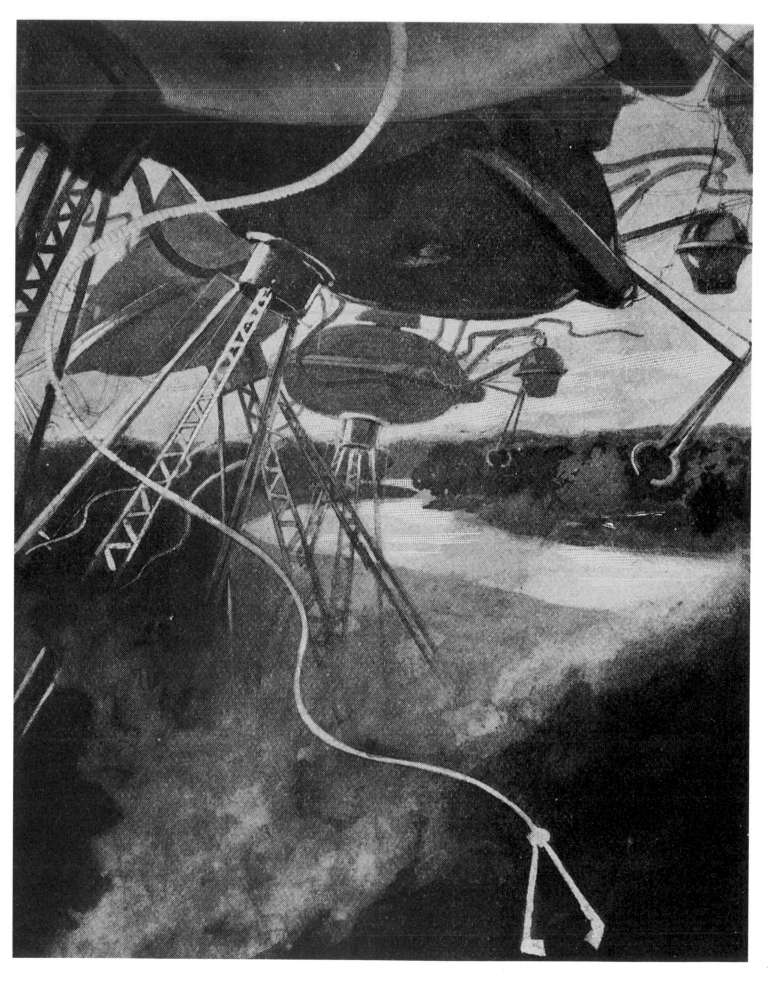

The loopholes, inconsistencies and potential paradoxes of these laws have provided Asimov with a *Leitmotif* and a livelihood. In *The Cybernetic Imagination In Science Fiction,* Patricia Warrick says of Asimov, "the drama he has created with the Three Laws has set us thinking. Perhaps in the real world ethical concepts could be operationalized in computer technology. No other science-fiction writer has given the world that vision." Asimov, in fact, writes about humans and human dilemmas through robot eyes and android problems.

A figure of equal significance and comparable output is Robert Heinlein, who, in his 1942 story *Waldo* gave an alternative name to telechirs, and in 1948 published *The Moon Is A Harsh Mistress,* in which a Moon-based computer achieves intelligent consciousness as the result of its memory and functions increasing beyond a certain critical size. Surely the WISARD team (see page 91) had read this, and dreamed of chatting with Mike (real name MYCROFT: an acronym nodding towards Sherlock Holmes' mysterious older brother) while he lobs boulders at non-human targets on invading Earth, or cycles the temperature and pressure in the Warden's apartment (the Moon colony is, in fact, a prison) causing the WCs to reverse their action. A better, more likeable model of robotic intelligence could hardly be devised. Heinlein may be subversive of reactionary authority, but for all his avowal of "rational anarchism," his *Starship Troopers,* featuring exoskeleton-clad intergalactic grunts, is a simplistic paean to militarism and New Order discipline. It's also a rattling good read, of course, and inspired the up-and-coming Harry Harrison to a malicious but affectionate parody some years later in *Bill, The Galactic Hero.*

Clifford D. Simak has been an elegant chronicler of future history in dozens of outstanding sci-fi stories and novels. In *City,* a thematic collection of 1940s short stories published in 1952, the central figures are Jenkins, robot butler to generations of the Webster family, and the dogs, intelligent talking canines descended from a Webster mutt used for brain-surgery experiments. While Jenkins goes uncomplainingly on through the collapse of human civilization on Earth, burying Websters, but keeping the Webster name and dreams alive, the dogs extend the bounds of animal and human knowledge with their extra-sensory perception of "things on the other side, the Cobbly Worlds," while keeping a sharp eye on the doings of the mutants, a hillbilly strain of super-intellects dedicated to having fun and frustrating the earnest ideals of fat-cat Websters and their Uncle Tom butlers wherever they roam. That the robots and the mutants might inherit the Earth, yet have sprung from it at human behest, is surely a potent expression of the dark side of that desire for immortality which gave the robot dream life in the first place.

Left *H. G. Wells' 1909 novel* The War Of The Worlds *enthralled its steam age readers with its descriptions of Martian rocket ships, death rays, and exoskeletal land cruisers. Thirty years later Orson Welles' Mercury Theatre radio presentation of the story in the form of a spoof newscast caused panic among ostensibly much more sophisticated Americans. Even today many of the ideas ring true, especially the ominous victory of Earth's microbes over the invaders — what that portends for the future of micro-biological warfare is unpleasantly easy to guess.*

Below *Early attempts to develop robot grippers were led astray by Robbie The Robot in* Forbidden Planet, *who broke new ground in vision systems with his converted toaster.*

Left *A young roboticist begs Der Golem for the secret of his serious hairdo; unspeaking, he tries to remember the universal hand-sign for "clay".*

Right *The progenitor of* Der Homunculus *(meaning "android of restricted growth") broods eloquently in the 1915 six-part robot soap.*

Robots in Films

European film-makers were drawing on the robot heritage from the early days of film. In 1897 Georges Méliès made *The Clown And The Automaton.* In 1914 Paul Wegener made the still-chilling *Der Golem,* repeating the theme in two later films in response to popular demand. In 1915 a six-part film serial called *Der Homunculus,* made by an unknown crew, appeared in Germany. A 10 minute version of *Frankenstein* was made in 1910, but the definitive statement of the monster epic appeared in 1931, Boris Karloff turning in an unforgettable performance of menace and angst as the monster. Over thirty remakes and rip-offs (we call them "homages" with a French accent in our critiques of The Film) have been made since, though they never replaced Boris.

A classic of film, a Futurist manifesto and a robot Mona Lisa combined to make Fritz Lang's *Metropolis* the most significant generator of the robot image, though its beautiful archetype, Mad Prof Rotwang's Machine — a seductive robotic prison for the soul of the lovely Maria — is actually a personification of evil. Being Art, the film is not, of course, About Robots, but is rather A Statement About Beauty, Power and The Soul.

The bad exposure that robots were starting to get from *Metropolis* and *Frankenstein* was powerfully offset by the bumbling avuncularity of the Tin Man in the magical 1939 *Wizard of Oz.* How satisfactory that the WISARDs of Brunel University in the 1980s should manage to construct a very passable brain, the subject of the Scarecrow's quest.

Bathed in the warmth of the Tin Man's quirky smile and the Wizard's parting admonition to "Remember...the heart is not judged by how much you love, but by how much you are loved by others," audiences in the 1940s could hiss and shiver and throw popcorn at Gort, the clanking low-tech hero of the 15-part serial, *Mysterious Dr. Satan.* Surely the first, and one of the best, of the punk cheapo robot villains, thrown together out of the studio junk and creative departments' wastebins, Gort deserved better than the classic romantic denouement of destroying his evil genius.

The next significant screen robot was very far from Gort's Brando-like brooding knowledge of Good and Evil; this was Robbie The Robot, star of the 1957 *Forbidden Planet,* a mechanical creep sucking up to Whitey and buying easy popularity by distilling bourbon. He reappears in the exploitation sequel, *The Invisible Boy,* but he's still just Andy Hardy in a central-heating unit, though still appearing in sci-fi and horror films today.

In 1962 Britain's BBC began televising its children's sci-fi soap, *Dr. Who,* which remained in production until its 1985 cancellation. Noted equally for its powerful signature tune (produced artificially in the BBC Radiophonic Workshop by Ron Grainer, it remains the only piece of electronic art to have gained and retained instant mass popularity) – and its shabby production values, the series has introduced a stream of memorable space villains, chilling despite their opera buffa settings. Most rabid among them are the Daleks, tiny lizard-like organisms who ride around in their ground-skimming vehicle-carapaces, bumping into things and squawking "EXTERMINATE!" in really unpleasant electronic tones — they're not actually evil, just the victims of unimaginative programing.

Opposite *The most powerful of robot myths in the person of the definitive robot-monster-as-hapless-victim: Boris Karloff weaves spells as the Monster in* Frankenstein.

Right *Maria, robot star of* Metropolis, *resists manipulative male directions in her search for the robotic role, and is cast thereafter as the very breath of evil given form; her tormentor, mad Rotwang, noted slave-trader and egomaniac, is remembered as misguided, perhaps too easily led?*

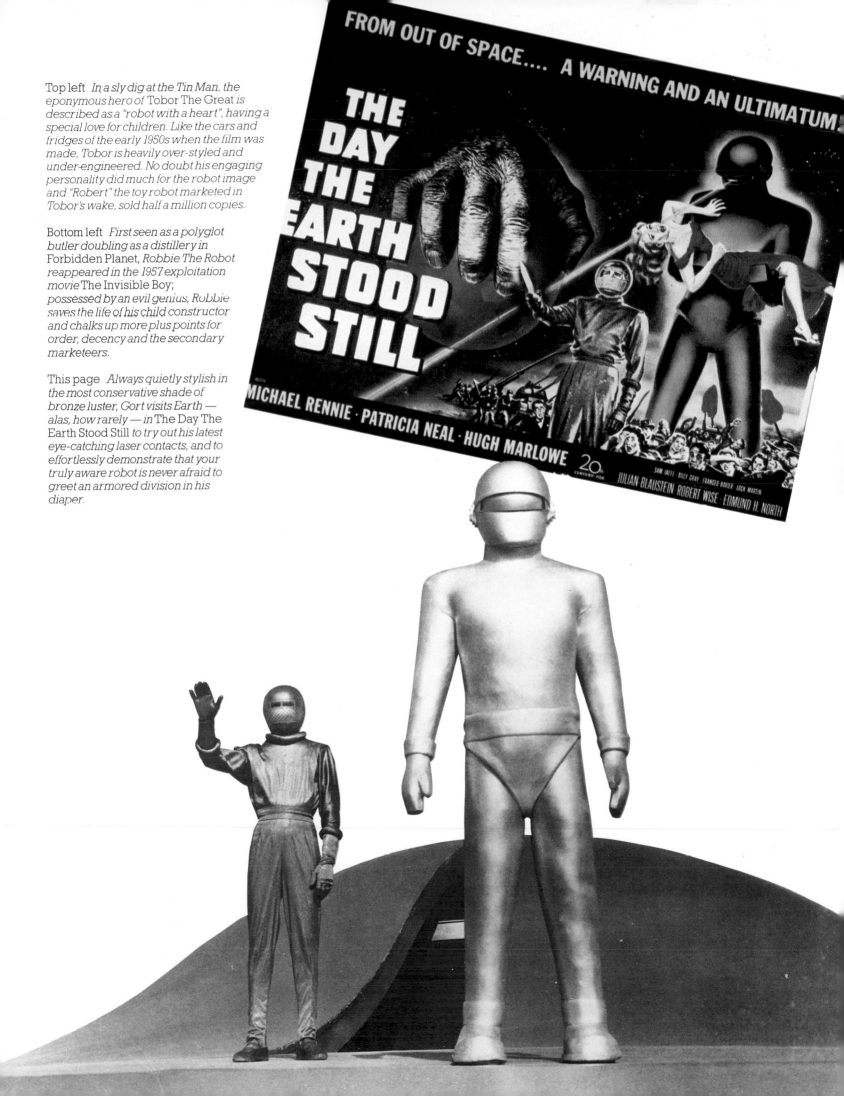

Top left *In a sly dig at the Tin Man, the eponymous hero of* Tobor The Great *is described as a "robot with a heart", having a special love for children. Like the cars and fridges of the early 1950s when the film was made, Tobor is heavily over-styled and under-engineered. No doubt his engaging personality did much for the robot image and "Robert" the toy robot marketed in Tobor's wake, sold half a million copies.*

Bottom left *First seen as a polyglot butler doubling as a distillery in* Forbidden Planet, *Robbie The Robot reappeared in the 1957 exploitation movie* The Invisible Boy; *possessed by an evil genius, Robbie saves the life of his child constructor and chalks up more plus points for order, decency and the secondary marketeers.*

This page *Always quietly stylish in the most conservative shade of bronze luster, Gort visits Earth — alas, how rarely — in* The Day The Earth Stood Still *to try out his latest eye-catching laser contacts, and to effortlessly demonstrate that your truly aware robot is never afraid to greet an armored division in his diaper.*

FROM OUT OF SPACE.... A WARNING AND AN ULTIMATUM!

THE DAY THE EARTH STOOD STILL

MICHAEL RENNIE · PATRICIA NEAL · HUGH MARLOWE

20th CENTURY-FOX

SAM JAFFE · BILLY GRAY · FRANCES BAVIER · LOCK MARTIN

JULIAN BLAUSTEIN · ROBERT WISE · EDMUND H. NORTH

In 1968 sci-fi pics went box-office boffo. Stanley Kubrick's *2001*, based on *The Sentinel*, a 1950 sci-fi story by Arthur C. Clarke, set new standards of production and plotting for space opera. The computer controlling the spaceship in which the lackluster human stars set out to contact the alien civilization is really the star of the film. Called HAL (compare this with IBM) for "Heuristically Algorithmic," the computer is a gigantic neural net, taught to speak and to perceive by a Mittel-European scientist-tutor-nutcase. It, quite rightly, perceives the human crew members as threats to the success of the mission, and begins to "terminate" them. "He" is frustrated by the wily Dave Bowman, a space Benedict Arnold, who manages to lobotomize HAL, despite his calm, even-voiced attempts to persuade Bowman to the contrary: "Look Dave, I can see you're really upset about this. I honestly think you ought to sit down calmly, take a stress pill, and think things over. I know I've made some very poor decisions recently."

Opposite In an enthralling and somehow chilling scene, one of the spacecraft's crew — the least puny, last survivor — destroys from within the marvelous organic intelligence that made the spacecraft so much more than just a space liner. The computer HAL derived its intelligence from the multiplicity of its neural links, and the diversity of its experiences, both physical and linguistic. This is an uncanny preview from the 1960s of the work of the artificial intelligence researchers of the 1980s — in particular that of the WISARD project.

Below Rated by many film buffs — not all of them sci-fi fans — as the film of its decade, 2001 brought space, mega-computers, and alien intelligence into believable perspective, with its cool factual treatment of such semi-metaphysical experiences as the Star Gate. Perhaps the most significant aspect of the film was its treatment of humans as at best wayward savages, at worst unconscious pawns, in the hands of superior intelligences, one of them, at least, of human construction. The congruence of this view with the Trojan horse view of robots and artificial intelligence added to the film's portentous burden.

Opposite Westworld's *robot gunfighter convinces his human customers and programers that a hardware fault has turned him and other robot fantasy toys into merciless killers, but robot buffs are not fooled, they know star quality when they see it — Win this one for Gort, fellas!*

Left *Hector,* first of the Demigod range *of robot supermarket trolleys, would like to be the villain of* Saturn Three, *but was mistaken for a multi-gym at the auditions.*

Equally inventive, and made on a fraction of the budget, John Carpenter's 1974 *Dark Star* features another talking computer-spaceship-robot, but this craft has all the appeal of those airport public-address machines that tell you your plane's going to be four days late; this one, though relentlessly "charming," nonetheless refuses to indulge the crew's sexist fantasies: "these mental conceptualizations of me as a smooth-skinned, pliant, and heavy-breathing female humanoid are neither healthy, nor conducive to the smooth operation of the ship. I must ask you to discontinue them." The thermonuclear bombs which the crew drop on unstable planets around the Galaxy are robots themselves, and converse amiably with the ship's computer and the crew: "I'm looking forward to carrying out the mission for which I was designed." As the result of machine literal-mindedness and human error, one of the bombs still attached to the ship begins its detonation countdown, which the commander tries to reason it out of by teaching it phenomenology. Unfortunately, the machine runs ahead of its mentor,

articulates Descartes' famous maxim (see page 13), and explodes. This is the first believable sci-fi pic with conscious humor and it survives very well to this day, in its script, its direction and its special effects.

Similarly quirky, though with rather more of a self-conscious message, Douglas Trumbull's 1972 *Silent Running* also features a deep-space mission of alienated humans, this time the guardians of Earth's last forests, preserved from terrestrial pollution in the space-craft's giant plastic domes. When the order comes to destroy the forests and return home, one of the crew, the obsessive solitary eco-freak, deserts with the ship, the forests, and three robot homunculi called Hewey, Dewey and Louie. These appealing little chaps help with the forestry and provide company and affection for the lonely human. When Nemesis arrives in the shape of another Earth mission, the forests are despatched into deep space in the care of the robots — better guardians of Humanity's better nature than Humanity itself. "Take good care of the forest, Dewey..."

Above left *The robot policemen from* THX
118 *are only too believable an aspect of a not-
too-distant future society wherein the robotic
principles of control and feedback are
elevated to the status of moral precepts.*

Above right *A less obviously baleful, though
morally more equivocal, vision of a robotic
society was* Westworld, *a latter-day
Disneyland in which robots obligingly acted
out the stage-managed fantasies of corrupt
self-indulgent human guests.*

Right *In* Futureworld, *the engaging
exploitation sequel to* Westworld, *the
principles of telechirics are brought to the
fore in the Palace Of Fun: the human guests
animate the various robot sideshows
through waldos placed around the booths.*

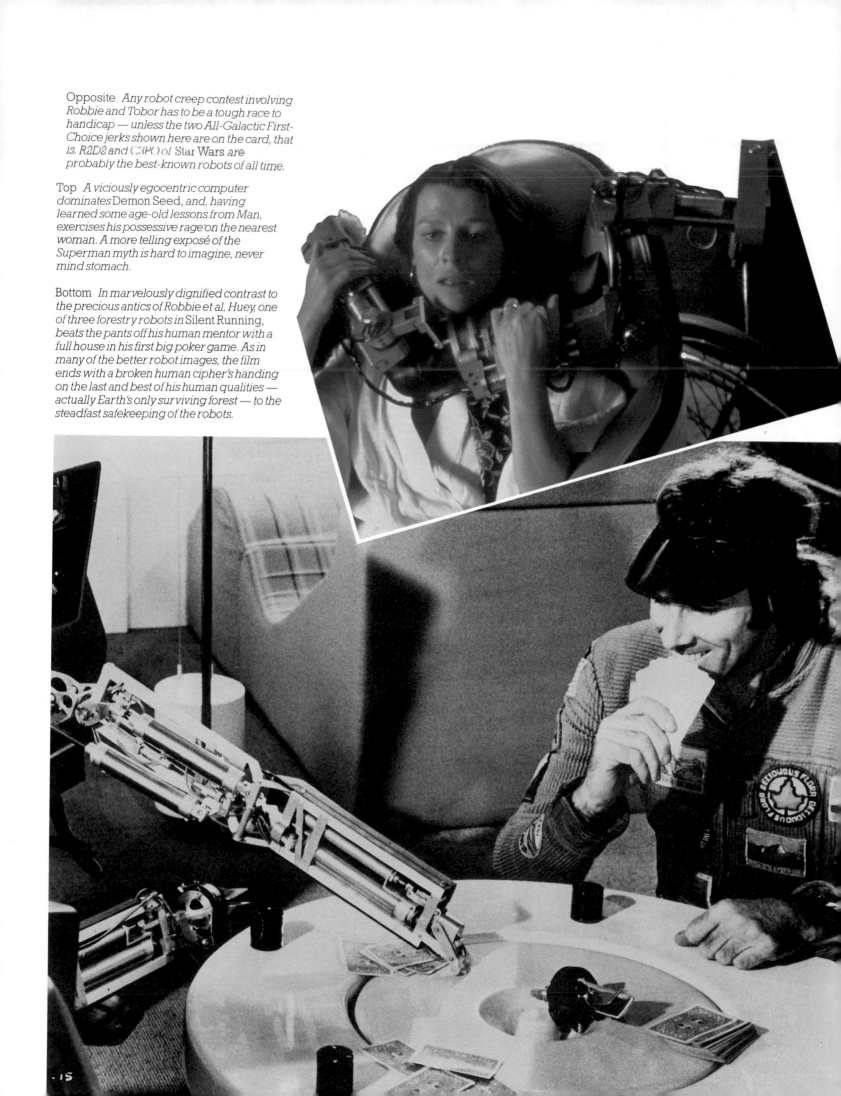

Opposite *Any robot creep contest involving Robbie and Tobor has to be a tough race to handicap — unless the two All-Galactic First-Choice jerks shown here are on the card, that is. R2D2 and C3PO of* Star Wars *are probably the best-known robots of all time.*

Top *A viciously egocentric computer dominates* Demon Seed, *and, having learned some age-old lessons from Man, exercises his possessive rage on the nearest woman. A more telling exposé of the Superman myth is hard to imagine, never mind stomach.*

Bottom *In marvelously dignified contrast to the precious antics of Robbie et al, Huey, one of three forestry robots in* Silent Running, *beats the pants off his human mentor with a full house in his first big poker game. As in many of the better robot images, the film ends with a broken human cipher's handing on the last and best of his human qualities — actually Earth's only surviving forest — to the steadfast safekeeping of the robots.*

"More human than human" is the motto of the android manufacturers in Bladerunner. Based on Philip K. Dick's novel, Do Androids Dream Of Electric Sheep?, it explores the familiar twin themes of robot-human enmity and human-robot love. Superstrong outlaw androids called "Replicants" (Left) return to Earth from their space colonies incognito, in an echo from Arthur C. Clarke's elegaic novel, Childhood's End. A private eye (all of cinemas' Sam Spade and Phillip Marlowes in one, the "Blade Runner" himself) given the job of tracing and exterminating them, grapples with their strength, intelligence and hatred while falling in love with one them, the lovely Rachel — surely Maria of Metropolis in the twenty first century? The genius of the original android creator has been perverted by crass commercialism into the production of freaks and sex toys as well as these dangerous Replicants, but he helps the runaways to evade pursuit, moved partly by paternal instincts towards his robot offspring.

The present, of course, belongs to the detestable R2D2 and C3PO of George Lucas' 1977 *Star Wars*. This cosmic Abbott and Costello are the final triumph of the confectioner's art, and represent all the sycophantic Tommism, all the po-faced non-conformist lollygagging Robbism, that Gort and HAL died to deliver us from.

Perhaps all is not lost, though: we do still have Douglas Adam's 1978 British radio space opera, *The Hitchhiker's Guide To The Galaxy*, in which appear both Marvin the Paranoid Android ("Brains and training enough to run a planet, and they make me pick up pieces of paper") and the book itself. This talking vademecum, the product of the cynical Sirius Cybernetics Corporation, who define a robot as "Your Plastic Pal Who's Fun To Be With," produces in the friendly, colloquial style of the popular science presenter, suspect and biased misinformation about Life, The Universe and Everything. The book has inspired several books, a TV series, a computer game, a film in production from Ivan "Ghostbusters" Reitmous, and a British Top Twenty success for Marvin's own first waxing. Unmoved by stardom ("I think you ought to know I'm feeling very depressed") and unfooled by his human companions' philosophical posturings ("Life? Don't talk to me about Life"), Marvin is the alternative zeitgeist, sal-ammoniac to C3P0's egg-nog, the true Person Of Steel. The robot image is safe with him.

Left *Everywhere the special effects are the stars of most sci-fi movies, a tradition proudly expounded in* The Black Hole.
Below *Vincent, the panty-waist robot butler of Disney's* The Black Hole *packs a rod on his captain's orders.*

Opposite *A dressy style and stovepipe arms mark the robot custodians of* Logan's Run *as real movers in robotic fashion circles.*

Left *Robot myth and classical fairy story seem to mingle in* Heart Beeps, *a tale of action-packed robotic romance among the chintzy environs of a secret government organ transplantation research center.*

A Robotic Future

*"Technology . . . the knack of so arranging
the world that we don't have to
experience it" — Max Frisch*

There are two aspects to the robotic future: the future of humans in a world increasingly peopled by robots, and the future of robots themselves. The latter is the easier, and less disturbing to dwell on. The former is potentially gloomy, overshadowed by fears of unemployment and massive social breakdown, a vision somehow more consonant with the mood of the times than any optimistic idyll of cultured human ease in the midst of placid robot plenty. It's a lot easier to forecast the technology of fifty years hence than it is to predict the political complexion of the 1995 Senate, and a lot less important.

The robotic developments of the past half-century have brought the science to the point where it can begin to live up to its claims, and to fulfil the public's expectations. Manufacturing will be increasingly automated, factories will be designed by and for robot operation, people everywhere will have robot tools, robot machinery, robot colleagues. The home will resist the robotic surge for longer, partly for economic reasons, partly because the existing appliances of the affluent western household will take on robotic techniques without materially altering in appearance or function. Transport, the exploitation of raw-materials, undersea and space exploration will all benefit from the employment of robot vehicles and intelligence. The streets of our towns may begin to take on an odd quiet as faceless electric robot vehicles roll silently past the robot traffic cops and parking wardens on every corner, through streets patrolled by Justice Department crime-watch robots, to the fortified homes of the wealthy, guarded by armed robot sentinels.

This is a millenarian view, not necessarily prophecy nor even projection, just social doodling. It follows, however, from our largely mechanistic view of the robot, as another tool, another technique. Despite the rich mythic structure of the robot heritage, no matter how often and how wryly we muse on the Doppelgänger and the Divided Self, still we are, as humans, a materialistic species; if a tool exists, we use it. Function, in fact, is not merely an aesthetic correlate, it is also a moral absolute. Consequently, though we will continue to worry about social change and economic divisiveness, nonetheless we will pick up the metal gauntlet, and employ the robot piecemeal but ever

more widely until suddenly we realize that the debate is over, there's no more question of controlling the robot's impact, or directing an industry's growth, because it's happened already. Like tobacco, like television, like the automobile, the robot comes neither to bless nor to curse, but simply to make somebody a buck or two; then before you know it everybody's got one, or wants one, or can't get rid of one, and the thing's a plague and a pest and A Real Social Ill.

We began the book by examining the bicycle as a harbinger of the Machine Age, and surely no one would want to have to decide the final reckoning of good and ill that these last hundred years have brought. It's a safe assertion, though, or non-controversial, at least, that the bicycle has not been among the curses of the era. The reasons for its neutrality — let us pitch it no more strongly than that — are worth considering.

The bicycle fits us, we are not hideously distorted or disturbed by riding one — neither physically nor mentally; it is not usual to experience on a bike the surges of pique, jealousy, anger, recklessness, hate and bile that are the emotional commonplace of driving a car. The bicycle does not demand huge amounts of material or energy in its construction or use. It does not confer disproportionately large benefits either, however; it does extend our reach as travelers, but it makes us dirty and smelly and hot at the same time. It extends our legs without supplanting them.

Right *Machines may save our labor but robots can go further and save our lives if they can be persuaded to fight for us in war. Artist Alan Daniels conveys profound sympathy for this near-human warrior who is mortally wounded in combat in deep space.*

Left *The real robotic future will see sensor and movement techniques incorporated in everyday devices; this sailing boat is SKAMP, Station Keeping And Mobile Platform. Uncrewed and wind-powered, it sails to, and maintains position at, any given spot by a combination of aerofoil sails and "satnav" location equipment.*

Top *The depths of the ocean are as ripe for robot exploitation as the far reaches of the Solar System. This US research submersible employs robot manipulator and location technology.*

Bottom *As city life grows more complex and crowded, the need for large-scale control of environment and equipment will demand robotic hands at the helms of trains and boats and planes everywhere.*

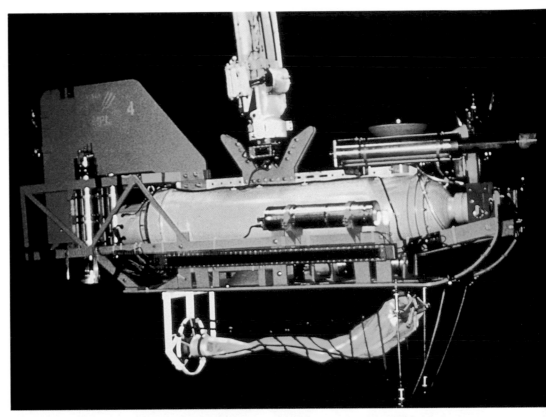

Left *The robot keyboard player's fingers, and the whole robot itself, are less significant as a musical development than as the endpoints of massive research into movement, control and vision systems.*

Bottom *The robot's dramatic looks and its musical virtuosity allows its manufacturers scope for the most grandiose publicity stunts, as this symphonic grotesquerie plainly shows.*

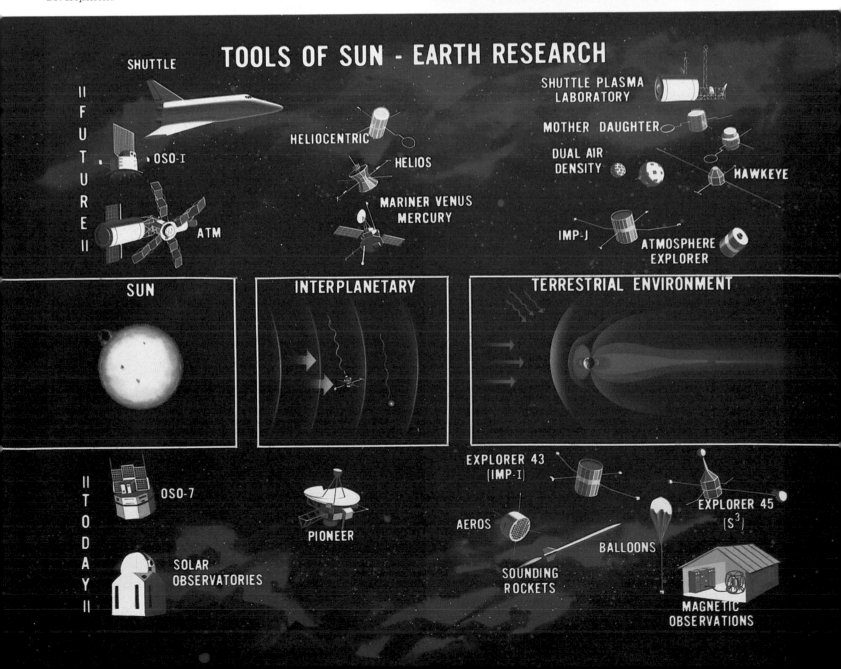

Right The years of intensive research into high-speed real-time control systems undertaken by roboticists have been gratefully embraced in such hi-tech aerospace hardware as NASA's HIMAT pilotless plane. There's more than a hint of Buck Rogers in the design philosophy, it seems.

Below At the edges of the atmosphere or beyond, robots and robotics are the most important tools of research, exploration and development.

TOOLS OF SUN - EARTH RESEARCH

FUTURE

SHUTTLE

OSO-I

HELIOCENTRIC

HELIOS

MARINER VENUS MERCURY

ATM

SHUTTLE PLASMA LABORATORY

MOTHER DAUGHTER

DUAL AIR DENSITY

HAWKEYE

IMP-J

ATMOSPHERE EXPLORER

SUN

INTERPLANETARY

TERRESTRIAL ENVIRONMENT

TODAY

OSO-7

PIONEER

SOLAR OBSERVATORIES

AEROS

EXPLORER 43 (IMP-I)

SOUNDING ROCKETS

BALLOONS

EXPLORER 45 (S³)

MAGNETIC OBSERVATIONS

The robot will become an ever more familiar figure in the landscape, though in rather less obtrusive colors one might hope. That its environmental impact be restricted to the visual is an outcome devoutly to be wished.

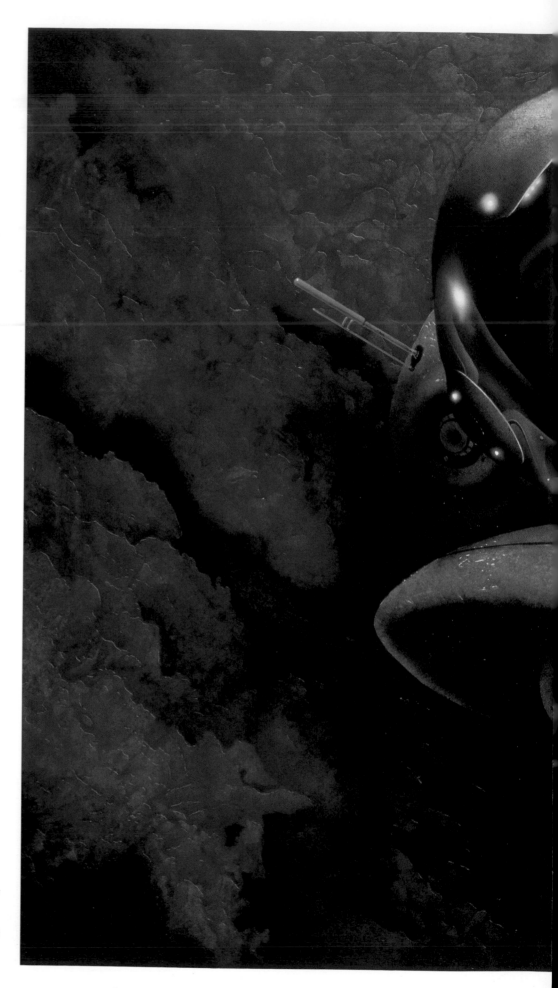

Telechirs are devices that extend the action of a human limb to a scale or an environment that is beyond the range of human performance. Inside this telechir an astronaut contemplates his next maneuver on the surface of an asteroid.

JIM BURNS '81

155

Left *If ever these deep space metropoles are to be built, it will be by robot roustabouts under robot gangers, crew chiefs and technicians, probably under the supervision of human architects and designers. Since space is so deadly for humans, however, and the cost of overcoming Earth's gravity so high, it seems unlikely that there would ever be a human population for these Wheelworlds — in which case, why build them? Robots don't need gravity, or shelter or bathrooms or food or rest.*

Opposite *The technology exists now to build and equip this fearsome pair of robot starship troopers, admittedly at enormous cost and with dubious operational efficiency; such drawbacks have never stopped the deployment of any previous weapon system, however.*

When you see this Lost Platoon singing We Shall Overcome *outside your bunker, you know they mean it.*

Does the robot pass the bicycle test? Is it a benign natural extension of some existing human feature? Do its form and function reflect some aspect of the human proportions? Are its energy needs conservative and natural? Does the robot at work put us more or less closely in touch with the social qualities that we value?

It's difficult to see very positive answers to these questions, even if you subscribe to the Robot Cornucopia school of future history. The commercial issue seems settled already; robots have arrived — are a fact. The social issue, then, remains — will our experience of the world be improved if we all find that the tedious, repetitive work is taken out of it? Will we change robots to suit us — in the towns, on the streets, in the home? We didn't manage the automobile's arrival too well, nor nuclear power — have these things changed themselves more than they have changed us? Must we reinvent the horrors of the Industrial Revolution every fifty years or so, or could we use the robot to allow us a little peace and wisdom, a pastoral interlude? Or must those truckers roll, the factories roar, great tides of production beat down our arbors, stranding our pretty little boats of hope on yet another shingly bar ...

On the Moon, in space, on the moons of Jupiter, robot factories will churn out minerals and products for Earth's metal-starved economies. The laser reflectors and the smart bombs will circle the globe, as the asteroid trawlers will circle the Sun. And somewhere A Voice will whisper "Gort..." and some Little Lost Robot will scrawl on some plastibrik wall, "Der Golem Wieder Komms..."

Below *The importance in the mundane industrial world of the robot arm has a quite different significance in the wilder fantasies of the film-makers, the novelists and the other myth marketers. As yet, these are just vaporings, candy-floss whipped up from energy and hot air; the robots are not plotting their revenge in our sewers, neither are they suffering nobly under our corrupt and repressive yokes. The real robots are spraying radiators and handling molds, fettling and welding and grinding with never an independent thought ...*

Opposite *... And yet humanity has never before been content to abandon a good myth just because it didn't fit today's version of the facts; tomorrow's robot is a creature not simply of science and engineering strained through production economics, but also the product of folk-lore, wish-fulfilment, and zeitgeist. If the species that has trod the highest mountains and swum the sounding deeps is not to walk the Sands of Mars, it will be a remarkable break with our past if we do not ensure that something palpably made in our own image does.*

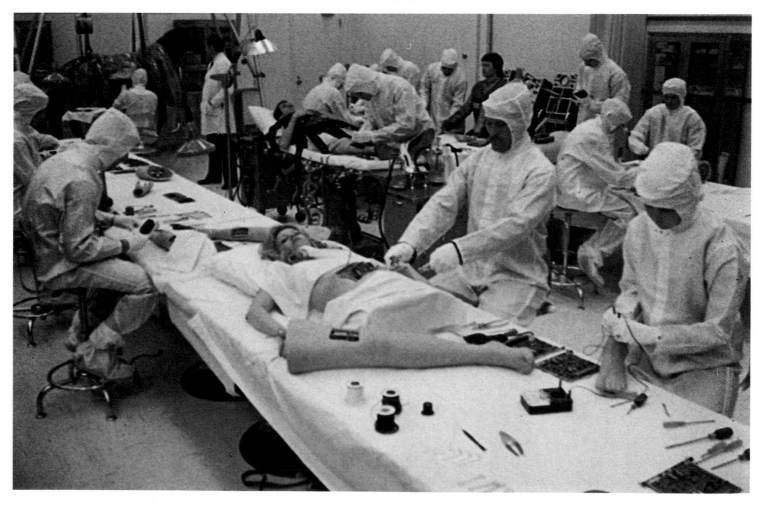

Appendix

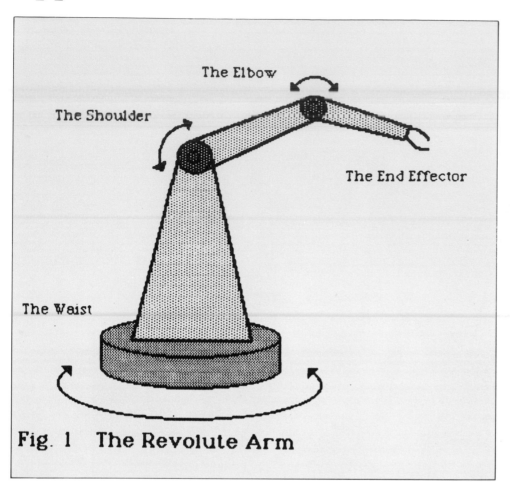

Fig. 1 *The revolute design contains three rotational joints and allows the arm maximum flexibility; a large number of points in the working envelope can be accessed in more than one way (with the elbow "up" or "down", but making the same angle between the upper and lower arms), a great advantage when the arm must work in a constricted or obstructed workspace.*

The Elbow

The Shoulder

The End Effector

The Waist

Fig. 1 The Revolute Arm

Fig. 2 *Replacing one of the rotational joints in the revolute design by a linear actuator gives the polar design. Here, the working envelope is a sphere centered on the shoulder joint. The advantage of this design over the revolute arm is that all the actuators can be placed close together and on the central axis of the robot; this greatly improves the weight distribution in the arm, allowing more of the power to be applied to the load rather than to the parasitic weight of the actuators.*

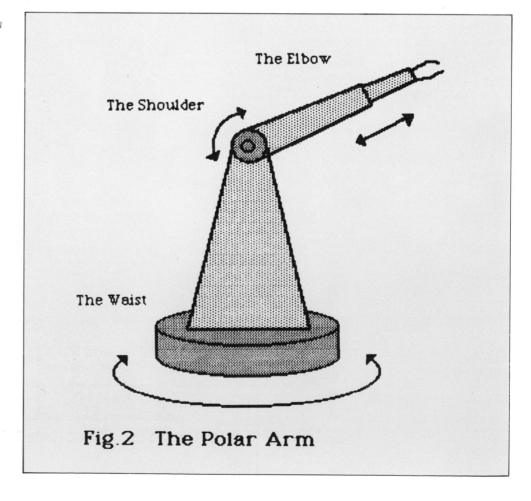

The Elbow

The Shoulder

The Waist

Fig.2 The Polar Arm

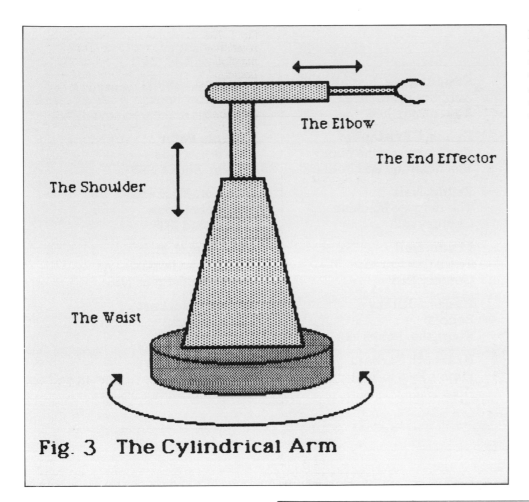

The Elbow

The End Effector

The Shoulder

The Waist

Fig. 3   The Cylindrical Arm

Fig. 3 *With two linear actuators and one rotational joint, the cylindrical arm's working envelope is a cylinder around the arm's central vertical axis. This is a restricted space, but suitable in many industrial applications where the arm is surrounded by easily accessible tasks at varying heights.*

Fig. 4 *The three linear axes of the Cartesian design make it ideal for many storage and retrieval tasks, and for "pick and place" applications in which the cuboid working envelope echoes the linearity of an assembly line or racking system.*

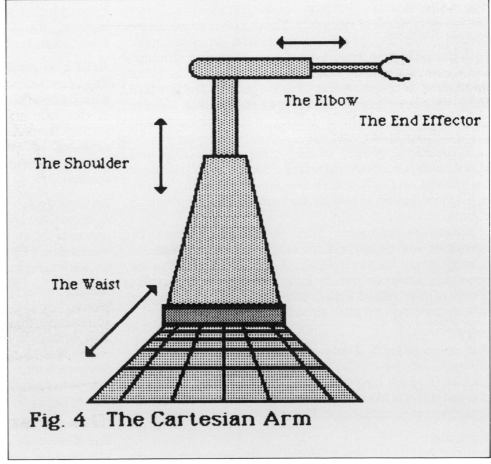

The Elbow

The End Effector

The Shoulder

The Waist

Fig. 4   The Cartesian Arm

Bibliography

Aleksander, Igor and Burnett, Piers
Reinventing Mann
Kogan Page 1983

Asimov, Isaac
I, Robot
Fawcett Books 1970

Boden, Margaret
Artificial Intelligence and Natural Man
Harvester 1977

Capek, Karel
RUR (Rossum's Universal Robots)
Doubleday 1923

Clark, William
Make and program your own Robots
Beaver Books 1985

Cohen, John
Human Robots in Myth and Science
Allen and Unwin 1966

Engelberger, Joseph
Robotics in Practice
Kogan Page 1981

Evans, Christopher
The Making of the Micro
Van Nostrand Reinhold 1981

Frude, Neil
The Intimate Machine
Century 1981

Frude, Neil
The Robot Heritage
Century 1984

Henson, Hilary
Robots
Kingfisher Books 1981

Krasnoff, Barbara
Robots Reel to Real
Arco 1982

Malone, Robert
The Robot Book
Harcourt Brace Jovanovich 1981

Marsh, Peter
The Robot Age
Sphere Books 1982

Pawson, Richard
The Robot Book
Windward 1985

Warring, R. H.
Robots and Robotology
Lutterworth Press 1983

Wiener, Norbert
Cybernetics
MIT Press 1947

Wiener, Norbert
The Human Uses of Human Beings
Houghton Mifflin 1950

Glossary

Actuator
The motive power units of a robot; the devices that power the moving parts of the robot. These devices might be electric motors, hydraulic actuators, or pneumatic actuators. Electric motors are clean, quiet, and efficient, but are relatively heavy and have to be sited on the robot itself, thus decreasing the power available for the task load. Stepper (qv) or servo (qv) motors are usually employed on low-load robots — in hobbyist and educational use, for example.

Hydraulic actuators are, by comparison, dirty and noisy, but the compressor (which does the work) need not be carried on the robot, so the parasitic loading on the arm is low. These actuators are found on most industrial robots.

Pneumatic actuators have the same virtues as hydraulic, but because air is much more compressible than hydraulic transmission fluid, pneumatic systems are generally less positive in location than the hydraulic. They are used where a clean environment is important, or where compressed air is already available.

AGV
Autonomous Guided Vehicles are semi-robotic vehicles, not quite remote-controlled, but not free to roam, either; usually they are delivery trucks in factories, and follow pre-set paths printed or coded into the floor. They may be equipped with collision detectors.

Android
A robot that looks like a human being, perhaps having simulated skin. In fiction, the android is the commonest form of robot, and evokes the most dread; in fact, the believable android does not yet exist, nor is there much commercial reason to invent it.

Artificial Intelligence
The branch of computer programing that attempts (so far with limited success) to reproduce the human attributes of decision-making, self-correction, and hypothesis testing. Researchers have devoted much AI effort to the problem of programing computers (and, therefore, robots) to understand natural language, especially speech.

Automation
An automatic mechanical device that lacks the power to process input information, a robot without sensors. Vaucanson's Duck, or a music box, or a clockwork robot toy, are examples.

Binary
Having two states. Most often used to refer to the binary number system in which there are only two digits, 0 and 1. This system is convenient for describing the logic of computers since they consist essentially of switching devices; switches have two states, ON and OFF, so the position of a switch can be represented by one of the two binary digits, 0 and 1.

Cartesian Design
The design of a robot arm consisting of three linear actuators (qv); its working envelope (qv) is a cuboid.

Continuous Path Movement

A robot arm can be taught (by a human operator whose actions it follows) or programed to perform movements exactly, as in welding or paint-spraying, for example. This is more difficult for the robot than point-to-point movement (qv), since it may require the arm to make movements involving more than one joint at a time: imagine a revolute arm's tracing a straight line, for example.

Cybernetics

The science of control. Invented by Norbert Wiener, it springs from his study of feedback in organisms and machines. In the hands of some of his followers, it has taken on the prescriptive powers of an ideology or a social theory.

Cylindrical Design

The design of a robot arm consisting of two linear actuators (qv) and one rotational actuator. Its working envelope (qv) is a cylinder.

Degrees of Freedom

The number of different ways in which the joints of a robot (usually a robot arm) are free to move; the human elbow, for example, has one degree of freedom, while the wrist has three.

End Effector

The device on the end of a robot arm. It should not be called a robot hand since it may take any form — from a wrench to a laser.

Exoskeleton

A powered framework worn by a human to amplify movement or power.

Feedback

The control information that is input to a system from its output — a thermostat, for example — feeds back the temperature of a system so that temperature in the room or in a car's cooling system can be controlled.

Flexible Manufacturing Systems

The complete industrial robot package: a system of robots and software that can be arranged in a workplace to perform a given task, but can then be easily reprogramed and rearranged to suit new or changing demands.

Neural Network

An attempt by AI researchers to simulate human intelligence: memory chips are connected together analogously to the neural connections of the brain, and the network learns about its environment through its sensors, rather than being programed.

Pick and Place

Moving things from place to place: a mundane task that robot arms can do much better, more cheaply, than conventional equipment such as conveyor belts, cranes, or humans. Most robots in industry simply pick up objects from one process and place them ready for another.

Point-to-Point Movement

Robotic movement in which the robot chooses its own routes between the fixed points of its task. A pick-and-place robot, for example, might be programed to pick from one spot, and place in another, but be given no instructions about the path between them; a robot employing continuous path movement, however, would follow learned or programed routes in which every point was predetermined.

Polar Design

The design of a robot arm consisting of one linear actuator (qv) and two rotational actuators. Its working envelope (qv) is spherical.

Revolute Design

The design of a robot arm consisting of three rotational actuators (qv). Its working envelope (qv) is a sphere.

Robotics, The Three Laws of

Invented by the science-fiction writer, Isaac Asimov (who also coined the word "robotics" for the study of robots), the Laws supposedly govern the behavior of all autonomous robots:

1 A robot may not injure a human being, nor, through inaction, allow a human being to come to harm.

2 A robot must obey the orders of a human being, except where such orders conflict with the First Law.

3 A robot must protect its own existence, except where such protection conflicts with the First or Second Law.

Servo Motor

An electric motor combined with an angular position sensor: the length of the control signal sent to the motor determines the angular position of the motor shaft. Often used as a robot arm actuator (qv).

Stepper Motor

An electric motor often used as a robot actuator (qv) in which the shaft revolves in separate fixed steps rather than continuously. The shaft can, therefore, be positioned accurately by sending a given number of control signals to the motor.

Telechir

A remote-control device which repeats the movements of the operator. The skeleton arms used in handling radioactive materials from behind safety screens are a familiar example, but telechirs are also used by surgeons for delicate surgery (on nerves, or inside the brain, for example), and by microchip assembly workers.

Working Envelope

The space in which a robot is free to move: strictly speaking, the volume accessible to the tip of its end effector. This is determined by the geometry of the robot's joints — rotational joints imply cylindrical or spherical envelopes, while linear joints imply cuboid envelopes. The shape of a robot's envelope and its degrees of freedom are crucial in determining the tasks for which it is best suited.

PICTURE CREDITS

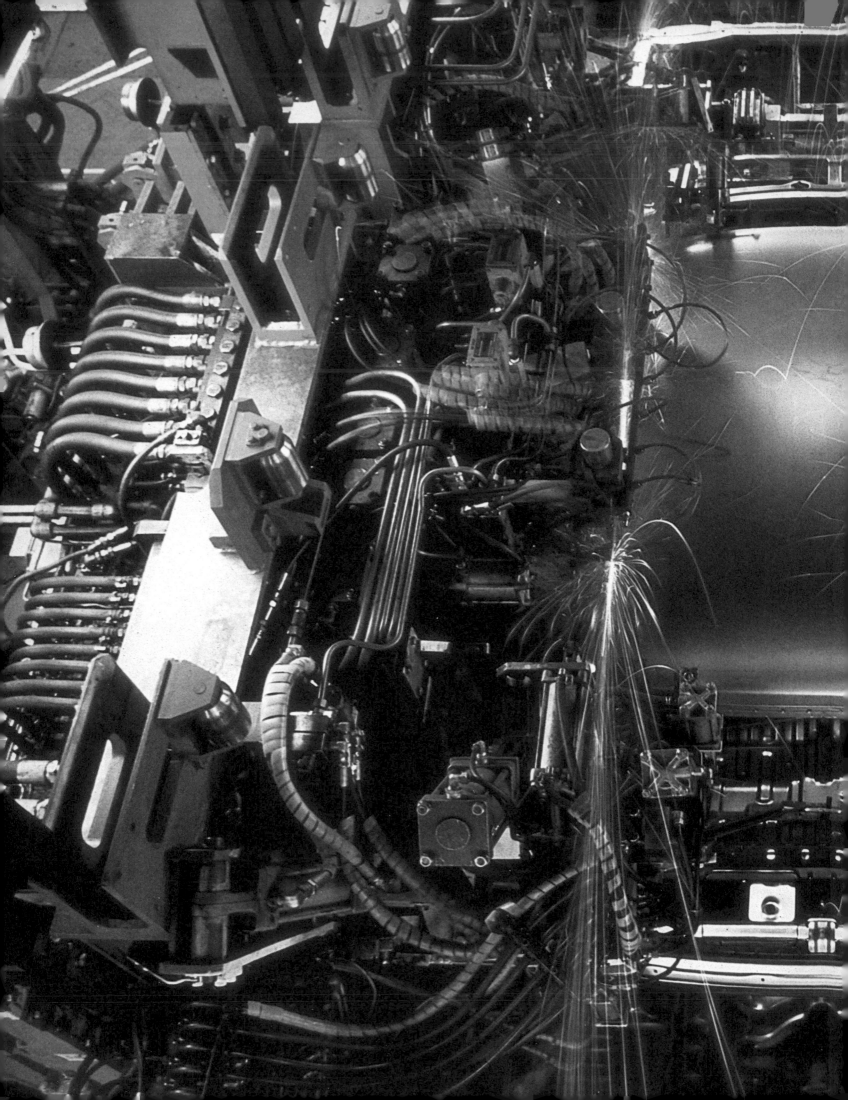